Ser

Longman Key Skills
titles available in the series

Application of Number Level 1+2
Application of Number Level 3

Communication Level 1+2
Communication Level 3

Information Technology Level 1+2
Information Technology Level 3

Pearson Education Limited
Edinburgh Gate, Harlow
Essex CM20 2JE, England
and Associated Companies throughout the world

First published 2000

British Library Cataloguing in Publication Data
A catalogue entry for this title is available from the British Library

ISBN 0-582-42486-0

Set by 3 in Sabon and Quay Sans
Printed in Great Britain by Henry Ling Ltd,
at the Dorset Press, Dorchester

Contents

How to use this book

This book helps you obtain the key skill called Application of Number at level 1 or level 2. You will be doing your key skills with your other studies in a school, college or at work. The common combinations are:

Level 1
GCSE and key skills
GNVQ Part One and key skills
GNVQ Foundation and key skills
NVQ1 and key skills

Level 2
GCSE and key skills
GNVQ Part One and key skills
GNVQ Intermediate and key skills
NVQ2 and key skills

An Application of Number key skill is not the same as maths. It is about knowing some facts about graphics, numbers or calculations and showing that you can actually use them in real life. Most of us need a reminder about some of those forgotten words and ideas so this book is organised to provide rapid help when you want it.

The good news about gaining any of the key skills is that you don't always need to do extra work. The evidence for the key skill is produced while you are doing your normal study and work such as in the classroom, laboratory, workshop, or while working at a job.

Of course there is a certain cunning in knowing which of your work to keep and how to show it, and that's what this is book is about. There are special sections for all popular GCSE and GNVQ subjects which tell you exactly what you need to do.

You can use this book in different ways; it depends on what you need. For example you might not need to read it from the beginning. To get the most out of this book, have a look at the following summary of how it is organised and decide how you can use it best.

The GNVQ Advanced awards are now called **Vocational A-levels.**

From September 2001 GNVQ Foundation and Intermediate awards are likely to be known as **Vocational GCSEs.**

Part 1: The Learning Curve

This part of the book concentrates on what you need to know to get the key skill units. It has useful information about graphics, numbers and how to use them in practical situations. It concentrates on the more tricky ideas and has clear worked examples to show you how to use them.

You can check that you have the basic knowledge needed by the key skill units. If you are up to speed with your maths then you may not need much of this section.

Everyone will find the **Useful knowledge** boxes helpful – they contain short reminders of important words and ideas.

Part 2: The Bottom Line

This part of the book tells you what you must do to gain the key skills units. It explains:

- The words and ideas of the key skills
- The difference between level 1 and level 2
- How you can practise the skills
- What must be in your portfolio of evidence

Your collection of evidence or portfolio is the key to getting your key skill. This part of the book tells you how to choose your evidence and get it ready.

Part 3: Opportunities

This part of the book tells you where to find opportunities for evidence in the study or work you are already doing. If you are at school or college you should look up the pages for your particular subjects at GCSE or GNVQ.

Everyone should look at the chapter on **Evidence from everyday sources**. It has examples of everyday activities we do at home, at work or at play that can also be used as evidence.

Margin

Look in the margin for simple explanations of important words and ideas and for references to other places in the book where there is useful information.

Part 1: The Learning Curve

This part concentrates on what you need to know to get your key skills qualification. It will show you:

- How to use numbers and graphics in practical situations.
- Whether you are up to speed with the basic knowledge needed for number key skills.
- Clear explanations of the more difficult ideas.

This part is divided into five sections:

- **Tables, charts, diagrams and graphs**
- **Numbers**
- **Data**
- **Measuring and observing**
- **Calculations**

You will also find the **Useful Knowledge** boxes helpful – they contain quick reminders of the most important words and ideas.

Tables, charts, diagrams and graphs

For quick reminders see the **Useful Knowledge** boxes.

This chapter shows you how tables, charts, diagrams, graphs or other displays work and how you can use them yourself. This way of presenting numbers or other information is called graphical or graphics.

You already use these graphics in your daily life when you read a bus timetable or look at a map. You need to know how to read and understand graphical displays so that you can also use them to present your own information. Such as the findings from your own investigations which can then be set out in a graph, chart or diagram.

Using tables

A table is a useful method of presenting information or data in a way that can be quickly and easily understood. A table consists of rows and columns, with headings and labels. The labels tell you what is stored in the table and help you identify what is being shown, such as travel insurance.

Step 2
Look down this column

| Period of cover | Travel insurance premiums (per person) | |
	Europe	Worldwide
4 days	£11.50	£40.50
9 days	£14.50	£48.00
17 days	£18.50	£53.50
24 days	£24.50	£58.00

Step 1
Look along this row

Step 3
Result

In this table we need to check the labels to know how the table works. For example, we might need insurance for a holiday of 2 weeks on a round-the-world trip. The table offers 9 days cover or 17 days cover, so we will have to choose the 17 days. Then starting with the 17 days on the left column we move horizontally along the row over to the column for Worldwide where we find the premium of £53.50.

Other types of table show data which can be turned into graphs or charts. Here is a table from a holiday brochure which shows the maximum temperature each month for different places in the world.

Temperature (°C)

	Jan	Feb	Mar	Apr	May	Jun	Jul	Aug	Sep	Oct	Nov	Dec
London	6	7	10	13	17	20	22	21	19	14	10	7
Miami	23	24	26	27	29	30	31	31	31	28	26	24
Sydney	26	26	25	22	19	17	16	18	20	22	24	25

Using charts

A chart is a diagram which shows relationships between numbers by using graphics. Charts are good at giving rapid visual information about data but their accuracy depends upon the size of their scales. A chart can also be misleading if it doesn't give you information such as where the starting point is. There are various types of charts such as pictograms, bar charts and pie charts.

Pictograms

A pictogram follows the same basic rules as other graphs but uses pictures or symbols to show the number of things that fall into a particular category. Instead of numbers on the horizontal scale you need to count the number of pictures. Usually one picture counts for more than one item.

Here is a pictogram which shows, for a certain group of people, the number of people travelling to each destination. Before counting the smileys, we need to read the information which tells us that each smiley on the pictogram stands for 2 people. So sometimes we may need to use half a smiley.

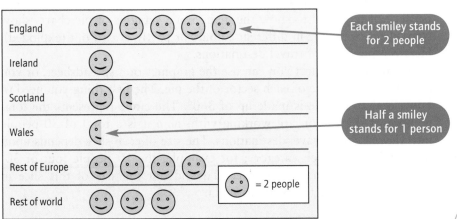

Each smiley stands for 2 people

Half a smiley stands for 1 person

= 2 people

Bar charts

Bar charts can have the bars vertical or horizontal.

Bar charts or bar graphs are another useful way of comparing information in a form that catches the eye. They are more accurate than pictograms as you can use a scale at the side to read more exact numbers. The following bar chart uses the height of the bars to compare the maximum daily temperature in London for different months. If you need to, you can read the actual temperature from the scale on the vertical side. The bars can be vertical or horizontal, they can be separated by spaces or placed next to each other.

Computer spreadsheets are designed to handle tables, graphs and charts. Enter your data in a table on the spreadsheet and the software allows you to display that data in a choice of charts and graphs.

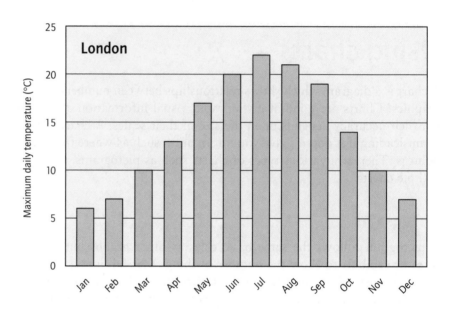

Pie charts

Full pie chart = 100% = 360°

A pie chart, as the name suggests, shows how information or data has been shared out. The chart always uses a circle which is divided into sectors (like the portions of a pie) to show how different amounts compare, or sliced up like a pie to show who has the most or the least. The full circle is 100% and the amount of each item shown is proportional to the angle or 'slice of pie' used to show the item. Some versions of pie charts show some slices of the pie in different colours or partly drawn out (exploded). Here is a pie chart of travel destinations.

To make a pie chart you can use the graphics of a spreadsheet, or you can calculate the size of each sector of the pie. The first thing you need to know is that a circle is made up of 360°. The circle represents the total number of things you are working with; here it is a total of 30 people interviewed about travel destinations. The size of each slice depends upon the numbers for each category; for example, the 10 people (out of 30) going to England make one slice. To find out the size of this slice in degrees you use the following formula:

$$\text{number of degrees} = \left(\text{number in category} \div \text{total number}\right) \times 360$$

For England:

$$\text{number of degrees} = (10 \div 30) \times 360 = 120$$

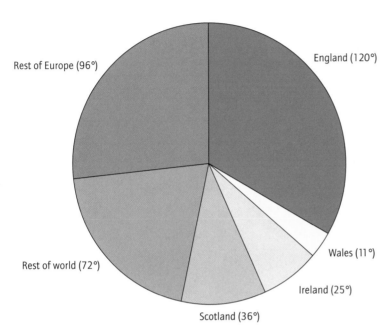

So the sector for England needs to be a slice which is 120° in size, out of a total of 360°. To measure 120° you will need to use a protractor and it should look like $\frac{1}{3}$ of a circle. It doesn't matter where you start a sector. You should also do a calculation like this for each category. Before drawing the pie chart a good way to check your work is to add up all the sectors. They should total 360°.

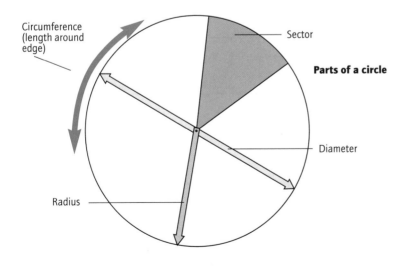

Parts of a circle

Frequency diagrams

Frequency means how many.

A frequency diagram is a form of bar chart. When information is collected for statistics, the frequency is the number of times a particular measurement occurs. The following table shows the travel destinations of a group of people. The number of people for each destination is the frequency of that destination. This information is often shown using a **frequency diagram**. In this case you can quickly see the popularity of a destination from the lengths of the bars.

A **tally** is a stroke on table that records the answer from one person. The fifth stroke is slanted to finish a group of a number. *See also*: **Data**, page 20.

Destination	Tally	Frequency
England	⦀⦀ ⦀⦀	10
Ireland	‖	2
Scotland	‖‖	3
Wales	‖	1
Rest of Europe	⦀⦀ ‖‖	8
Rest of world	⦀⦀ ‖	6
Total		30

Frequency is the total number for that destination

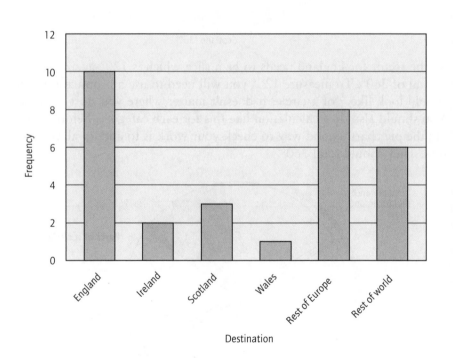

KNOW YOUR CIRCLES

Circle One complete turn makes a circle. This full circle contains 360 degrees (written 360°).

Diameter The diameter is the distance across the whole circle, passing through the centre.

Radius The radius is the distance from the centre to the edge. It is half the distance across the whole circle. If there are two or more, you refer to them as radii (pronounced ray-dee-eye).

Circumference The circumference is the curved line that forms the distance all the way around the edge of the circle.

Sector The part of a circle that is formed between two radii of the circle. It is like a slice of pie in a pie chart.

Pi Pi (symbol π) is the sixteenth letter of the Greek alphabet. In number terms it has a special meaning. It stands for the relationship between a circle's diameter and its circumference. It is often written as 3.14 (rounded to two decimal places) or $\frac{22}{7}$. Because of its special connection with circles, it is used in all the formulas that have to do with circles. For example, area of circle $= \pi r^2$

Using simple graphs

A graph is a type of diagram which shows how two different quantities relate to each other. The numbers are laid out on axes at the side of the graph and the relationship is shown by a continuous line. This line is often a straight line but can also be a curve for some relationships.

The graph is a good way of quickly finding information and also for changing from one unit to another. This temperature conversion graph shows how temperatures in degrees Celsius relate to temperatures in degrees Fahrenheit.

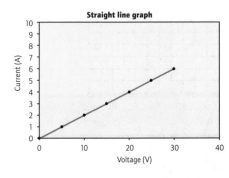

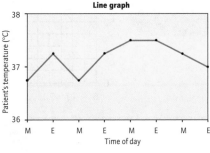

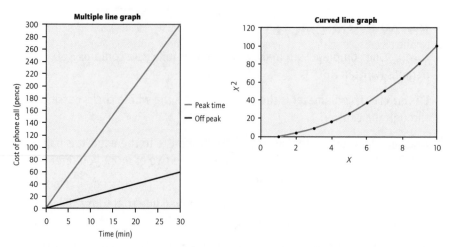

There are also formulas which convert between temperatures but using a line graph is usually quicker and easier. The example shows how you can convert 60 °C to 140 °F. You need to read up vertically from the 60 on the Celsius scale at the bottom and make a mark on the slanting line. From that mark you need to read across horizontally to the Fahrenheit scale on the side. Because the scale can't show every number, you will often have to read in between the scale and decide, using your eye, what the final answer is.

When you read a graph upwards or across you must make sure the reading is exactly vertical or exactly horizontal. Most graphs have a grid of lines to help you do this but if there aren't enough lines then use a ruler.

Axes: the two straight lines, at right angles, which have the scale of numbers.

x-axis: the horizontal scale.

y-axis: the vertical scale.

Scale: the numbers and spacing marked along the axes.

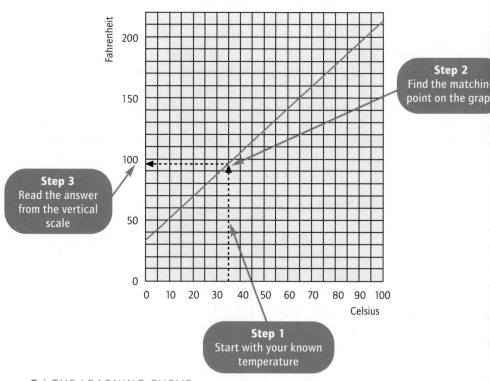

Take care! Although a graph is convenient to use, it is limited in accuracy by the size of its scale, and also depends upon how good *you* are at using it. Always check your reading by doing it again, to see if your get the same answer.

USEFUL KNOWLEDGE

Pictogram
Pictograms use symbols to show how many units of data belong in a group.

Bar chart
Bar charts use the length of a bar against a scale to show how many units of data belong in a group.

Frequency diagram
A graphical way of showing the number of things counted in each group or type. Bar charts and pictograms are frequency diagrams.

Pie chart
A circular diagram where each group is shown as a slice or sector and the size of each sector shows the number of things counted in that group.

Line graphs
Diagrams which show how information changes between consecutive values. The 'line' may be all straight, it may be straight between points on the graph, or it may curve.

Scatter diagram, scattergram, scatter graph
A diagram or graph which shows how two sets of numerical data are related. It is made by plotting matching pairs of numbers as points on a graph.

Axes
Graphs normally have two reference lines, called axes (one reference line is called an axis). They are drawn at right angles to each other. The horizontal axis is sometimes called the *x*-axis, and the vertical axis is often called the *y*-axis.

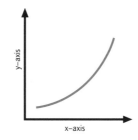

Variables
A variable is what you are measuring on your graph. You measure it because it can change – it is variable. For example, if you are showing temperature each month, you measure the temperature because it changes and you plot it against the month the measurement was taken in. The non-changing variable is usually put on the *x*-axis. In this example the months don't change so they make a good *x*-axis.

TABLES, CHARTS, DIAGRAMS AND GRAPHS | **9**

Numbers

See also: **Calculations**, page 28

This chapter shows you what numbers are and how they are used. You only need to know ten basic numbers or digits to be able to show any amount or to describe any size:

0	1	2	3	4	5	6	7	8	9

When we get to 10 we start to use a combination of these digits. We can use these digits to make many different types of numbers, such as decimals, fractions, very large numbers and negative numbers.

This chapter concentrates on using numbers in ways you are likely to come across in examples. A later chapter concentrates on calculating with numbers. The **Useful Knowledge** boxes have brief reminders of basic terms and ideas if you need them.

Writing numbers

There are only ten basic symbols but they can be used to write all the other types of number, including very large or very small numbers. Take care when writing numbers. Here are two rules to help you:

- **Lots of zeros:** put them in groups of three with a space between the groups. For 3 million you would write 3 000 000.
- **Column of numbers:** line up the decimal points, the tens, the hundreds and so on:

```
320.7
 43.1
  6.738
```

Some number types
whole numbers 20
even numbers 2, 8, 72
odd number 3, 11, 79
decimals 20.5
fractions $20\frac{1}{2}$
positive +20
negative −20

Make sure that you can also write a number in words, like the examples below. On a cheque you need to write the amount in figures and in words.

75	seventy-five
2750	two thousand seven hundred and fifty
3 275 000	three million two hundred and seventy-five thousand
0.75	zero point seven five
0.001	zero point zero zero one

> **Take care!** In some countries people use a comma to mark the decimal.

Shorthand signs

equals sign	=
decimal point	.
plus sign	+
minus sign	−
multiply sign	×
divide sign	÷ or /
percentage	%
ratio sign	:

Rules for numbers

You already know the basic rules for numbers – they are the following rules of arithmetic.

Rule	Signs
Addition or 'plus'	+
Subtraction or 'minus'	−
Multiplication or 'times'	×
Division or 'goes into'	÷

Every calculator has a button for these four operations as well as a few others such as percentage.

Negative numbers

We sometimes need to describe things with negative numbers, also called directed numbers. We use a + (positive) sign or a − (negative) sign to label things which can go below zero, or below some other starting point. The temperature of the weather is an example where temperature can go below zero degrees Celsius. Another example of negative numbers is a bank account. The money in your account can be positive (the bank owes you) or negative (you owe the bank).

With negative numbers, −5 is further away from zero than −2. This is not such a strange effect if you think in terms of owing money. Make sure you can calculate the difference in amount between these sorts of numbers.

What is the difference in temperature when the weather changes from −5 °C to +20 °C?

From −5 °C to zero the temperature rises by:	5 °C
From zero to +20 °C the temperature rise by:	20 °C
(usually we just write 20 °C and omit the +)	
The total of the two temperature rises is:	25 °C
Check this on the thermometer diagram	

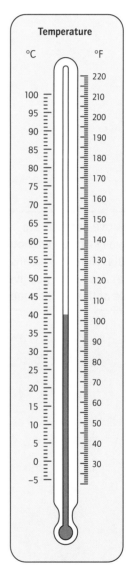

Temperature

°C   °F

> **Take care!**
> You now use the sign '−' as shorthand for two different ideas:
> - When used in 4 − 3 = 1 it is an instruction to subtract.
> - When used in −20 °C it indicates that the temperature is on the negative side of zero.

When you don't have a real scale like on a thermometer it is useful to make a **number line**. You can use it to help you place numbers in order and to add or subtract them.

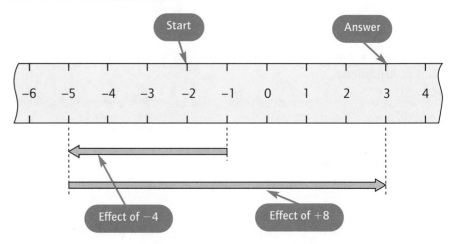

Find the result of combining −1, −4 and +8.
The number line shows how to work out the result:

- Start at the 21 position.
- For −4 move backwards (because negative) by 4 steps to the −5 position.
- For +8 move forwards (because positive) by 8 steps to the +3 position.
- So the answer is:

$$(-1) + (-4) + (+8) = +3$$

Positive numbers are usually written **without** a plus sign, so 3 means that 3 is on the positive side of the number line.

Fractions decimals and percentages

Fractions decimals and percentages are all different ways of showing that we only have part of a whole. For example:

One-half	$= \frac{1}{2}$	$= 0.5$	$= 50\%$
	fraction	decimal	percentage

You already know some of these relationships and it is worth remembering the following common ones. The decimals for one-third and two-thirds are given to 3 decimal places.

	Fraction	Decimal	Percentage
One-tenth	$\frac{1}{10}$	0.1	10%
One-quarter	$\frac{1}{4}$	0.25	25%
One-third	$\frac{1}{3}$	0.333	$33\frac{1}{3}\%$
Two-thirds	$\frac{2}{3}$	0.667	$66\frac{2}{3}\%$
One-fifth	$\frac{1}{5}$	0.2	20%

Working with fractions

Fractions of quantities can be found by dividing the quantity by the bottom half of the fraction and then multiplying by the top half of the fraction. It doesn't matter whether you divide or multiply first.

Find $\frac{3}{5}$ of 125.

First $125 \div 5 \ 5 = 25$
then $25 \times 3 = 75$
so $\frac{3}{5}$ of 125 is 75

Working with decimals

A decimal number uses the decimal point to separate the whole number (written on the left of the point) and the fractional part (written on the right of the point). Remember that a decimal with many digits needn't be a big number. For example, 22.4500 has 6 digits and 2245 has 4 digits, but 22.4500 is less than 2245.

Calculators often churn out many more numbers than make sense. So we need to decide, or to be told, how many decimal places (dp) to use. To reduce the number of decimal places we need to round off.

3.862 becomes 3.86 when expressed to 2 dp (rounded downwards)
3.86 becomes 3.9 when expressed to 1 dp (rounded upwards)

You should indicate how many decimal places you have used for writing down a number. For example 3.86 (2 dp).

Working with percentages

Percent means 'out of a hundred' and if you were given a 4% wage increase then for every £100 you would get an extra £4. To work out the percentages of numbers other than 100, use the following formula.

To find the percentage of any number
number × percentage rate ÷ 100 = percentage (%)

To write a number as a percentage of another number
(first number ÷ second number) × 100 = percentage (%)

To find 7% of 600.

Use number percentage rate ÷ 100 = percentage (%)
so $600 \times 7 \div 100 = 42$

To express 42 as a percentage of 600.

Use (first number ÷ second number) × 100
so $(42 \div 600) \times 100 = 7\%$

Remember that 10% is always the same as $\frac{1}{10}$ or dividing by 10. If a price

---

Parts of a fraction

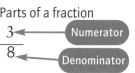

3 ← Numerator
8 ← Denominator

To add or subtract decimals
Place numbers in column; line up the decimal points; add or subtract as usual.
To multiply by 10
Move the decimal point to the right.
To divide by 10
Move the decimal point to the left.

---

dp is shorthand for decimal places.

For the rules of rounding up or down see the **Useful Knowledge** box, page 16.

ticket of £500 is increased by 10% then you need to find 10% of the original price and add it on:

$$10\% \text{ of } 500 = \tfrac{1}{10} \text{ of } 500 = 50$$

So the new price is $500 + 50 = £550$. If the price were reduced by 10% then you would subtract the 10% $(500 - 50 = £450)$.

Another well-known use of percentage is the interest rate paid to savers or charged to borrowers.

Comparing numbers

Sometimes we wish to compare the sizes of two numbers. There is a choice of methods, including fractions, percentages, proportions and ratios.

Ratio

We can compare any two numbers by writing them alongside one another separated by a ratio sign (:). For example, a juice/water mixture of 1:3 tells us that for every one measure of juice there are three measures of water. The usefulness of ratio is that we don't need to know whether the measure is a cup or a tank, as long as each measure is the same size.

We like ratios to be as simple as possible. The ratio of 6:10 can be simplified because 6 and 10 have a common factor of 2. Dividing by 2 it becomes 3:5. The trick is to divide both parts of the ratio by the *same* number so that the ratio remains true. The trick also works for fractions.

Ratios are often written with 1 as the first number. To achieve this then both numbers must be divided by the first number.

To simplify the ratio 3:5 and express it as 1:x.
Original ratio is   3:5
Divide each number by 3 to give $1:1\tfrac{2}{3}$
Which can also be written as a decimal   1:1.67 (working to 2 dp)

Ratios can have more than two parts. For example, a recipe for a fruit drink says that apple juice, orange juice and lemonade are to be mixed in the ratio of 1:2:4. Which means:

1 part of apple juice : 2 parts of orange juice : 4 parts of lemonade

It doesn't matter what you use to measure a part as long as you keep it the same. And you must match the right number of parts to the right ingredient – 1 part of apple juice, 4 parts of orange juice and 2 parts of lemonade will produce a different drink.

Accuracy

When you write numbers you need to decide the degree of accuracy. For example, £6.18 is accurate to 3 significant figures but £6 is accurate to 1

LEVEL 2

significant figure. For everyday work we only need 1 or 2 significant figures.

Rounding off

To write a large number with sensible accuracy you need to throw away the extra digits you don't need. Before throwing these digits away they are checked to see if you will round up the remaining digits. There are four rules of rounding:

- Find the position of the last digit.
- Look at the next digit to the right.
- If the digit to the right is 1 to 4, discard it and leave the last digit unchanged.
- If the digit to the right is 5 or above, discard it but increase the last digit by 1.

Write 3.141 592 65 to 4 significant figures.

Inspect number: 3.141 592 65

> This is the last digit, we must decide whether to leave it unchanged or to increase it by 1

> This is the digit to the right of the last digit, it is 5 therefore we increase the last digit by 1

Round number: 3.142 (4 sf)

Significant figures

The number 6 188 000 has 4 significant figures. If we round the number to the nearest million then the new number 6 000 000 has 1 significant figure. But notice that it is still a big number!

When we reduce the significant figures of a number we use the rules of rounding – check the rules of rounding in the **Useful Knowledge** box – and then use zeros to show the correct size of the number. When dealing with decimal numbers we use similar rules. Look at the following examples.

sf means significant figures.

Number	Significant figures	Notes
569	3 sf	
569 000	3 sf	Ignore the zeros at the end of a number
569 732	6 sf	
4003	4 sf	The zeros within the number do count
400 300	4 sf	Ignore the zeros at the end of a number
0.569	3 sf	
0.569 732	6 sf	
0.005 69	3 sf	Ignore the zeros at the front of the number

Rough calculations

Rough calculations or estimates involve you working out numbers in your head to give an approximate answer. You probably do this already.

You buy three cans of drink at 45p each: find the approximate cost.

    45p is approximately 50p

    3 times 50p is   150p   **You do this in your head**

So you expect the bill to be about £1.50. You would be surprised if you were asked to pay £13.50 instead of £1.35, the exact amount.

A simple rule for estimating is to round numbers to 1 sf. If the number is easy to deal with, like 25, then you might round to 2 sf. You need to be rather ruthless in keeping to the rule and not getting distracted by the smaller numbers. Look at the following example.

> The wavy equals sign ≈ means that an answer is approximate.

Estimate the result for 235.8 × 19.

    Simplify by rounding: 200 × 20 (using 1 sf)

    Multiply in your head: 4000

    So the estimated answer can be stated: $235.8 \times 19 \approx 4000$

USEFUL KNOWLEDGE

Numbers

We use numbers to write down measures of various types. Examples: 3 people, 24 degrees, 150 kilometres.

Digits or numerals

Digits are the symbols 0, 1, 2, 3, 4, 5, 6, 7, 8, 9. They are used in groups to make numbers such as 150, which is a number made of three digits.

Whole numbers

A whole number has no fractions, so 3, 24 and 150 are whole numbers but 3.5 is not a whole number.

Even numbers

An even number is a whole number which can be divided by 2 without leaving a remainder. Any number which ends in 0, 2, 4, 6 or 8 must be an even number. Examples: 4, 10, 14, 234.

Odd numbers

An odd number is a whole number which leaves a remainder of 1 when divided by 2. Any number which ends in 1, 3, 5, 7 or 9 must be an odd number. Examples: 3, 19, 327, 1001.

Adding and subtracting negative numbers

Draw a number line; for positive (+) numbers move to the right and for negative (−) numbers move to the left.

USEFUL KNOWLEDGE

Fractions

Fractions can be written with a horizontal line or a slanting line. One-third can be written $\frac{1}{3}$ (horizontal line) or ⅓ (slanting line).

The numerator is the number above the horizontal line (on the left of the slanting line) and the denominator is the number below the horizontal line (on the right of the slanting line).

Rounding numbers up or down

Find the last digit of your number then find the next digit to the right. If this digit is 1 to 4, discard it and leave the last digit unchanged: 452 becomes 450 when rounded to 2 significant figures. If it is 5 or above, discard it but increase the last digit by 1: 458 becomes 460 when rounded to 2 significant figures.

Percentages

To find the percentage of any number, use this formula:
number $\times$ Percentage rate $\div$ 100 = percentage (%)
To find 22% of 400 calculate 400 $\times$ 22 $\div$ 100 = 5%.

Data

The word 'data' means a set of measurements, or other numbers. Statistics depends on working with a reasonable number of measurements to see if there are trends or averages. Data can be shown in a variety of ways, including the graphs and charts in previous chapters. Data can be divided into two types:

- **Discrete data** is obtained by counting and can only have fixed numbers. For example, the number of cars passing a point. There are no fractions.
- **Continuous data** which can be any size of number within agreed rules. For example, the figures for heights of people or weights of people.

The word **data** can be used as plural and the word **datum** used as singular. But in modern statistics and computing it is alright to use the word **data** as singular and to write **the data is.**

Average values and spread

A set of data is a list of numbers, perhaps many hundreds of numbers, and we don't usually present this raw information. We need to summarise the effect of the data by using just a few numbers. The idea of an average value is to use just *one* number to give people a feeling for the centre of all the numbers in the data, such as the ages of people in a town.

However, a simple average value by itself may give you a wrong idea about the total effect of the data. Look at the data sets A and B. Both sets of data have the same average or central figure of 20, but they have different spreads or range. Data set A has a smaller or tighter spread of 4; data set B has a larger or more spread out range of 24.

Data set A (ages):	**18**	**20**	**22**
Average	= 20		
Range	= 4 (22 − 18)		

Data set B (ages):	**8**	**20**	**32**
Average	= 20		
Range	= 24 (32 − 8)		

To give a better summary of data we have a choice of methods, including a choice of average. A simple average is called a **mean** and there are additional ideas of **median** and **mode** which help describe the shape of the data. It is best to start using these statistical words accurately and you can look at the **Useful Knowledge** box to check the definitions if you need to.

Mean (average)

5	4	8	3	3	4	6	7	6	4	12

Mean is the most common type of average. Above is a set of 11 numbers: To calculate the mean, all the data is added up and the total divided by the number of items:

$$\text{Mean} = \frac{(5 + 4 + 8 + 3 + 3 + 4 + 6 + 7 + 6 + 4 + 12)}{11} = \frac{62}{11} = 5.6$$

The symbol for mean is $\bar{x}$.

Range

The simple example of ages on page 18 shows how two sets of numbers which have the same mean can be rather different in other ways. The range tells us the difference between the highest and the lowest values and is a simple indication that the spread is different.

Returning to the set of 11 numbers:

5	4	8	3	3	4	6	7	6	4	12

The range is found by inspecting the numbers to find the lowest (which is 3) and the highest (which is 12). The value of the range is then 12 − 3 = 9.

Mean is the central average value.
Median is the middle value.
Mode is the most popular value.
Range is the gap between smallest and largest.

Median and mode

To find the median you need to arrange the data in order from smallest to largest, then select the middle number. Let's use our set of 11 numbers:

5	4	8	3	3	4	6	7	6	4	12

Rearranging the numbers in order we get

3	3	4	4	4	5	6	6	7	8	12

To find the **median** you identify the number in the middle of the data set. It has the same number of items above it and below it. You can find the median by just looking and counting, but don't worry about the size of the numbers. Here the median is 5, because there are as many values above as below:

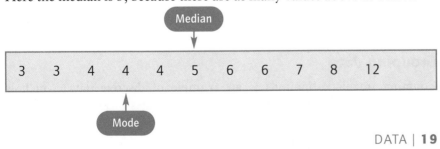

DATA | **19**

To find the mode you identify the value in the data set which occurs most often – it is the most popular number. Once again, this is done by eye and the answer is 4, because 4 occurs 3 times in the line-up.

> **Take care!** When rearranging the order of data from smallest to largest, don't lose any entries.

Collecting data

We often collect information by reading the scales on instruments or by observing and counting events. In all cases it is best to record this data on questionnaires or tables you have prepared in advance. To survey the travel destinations of a group of people, the following table needs to be drawn up in advance. Otherwise you will be trying to write down places and numbers and continually changing them.

Destination	Tally	Frequency
England		
Ireland		
Scotland		
Wales		
Rest of Europe		
Rest of world		
Total		

The **tally** is used by making one stroke for each item (destination) counted. The fifth stroke is drawn as a diagonal 'gate'; it stands for an item and it helps the eye count the strokes at a later stage. The **frequency** is the total number of times that you get a tally in a particular group (destination).

Destination	Tally	Frequency	
England	⦀⦀ ⦀⦀	10	Tally marks are crossed off in groups of 5
Ireland	‖	2	
Scotland	‖‖	3	
Wales	∣	1	
Rest of Europe	⦀⦀ ‖‖	8	
Rest of world	⦀⦀ ∣	6	
Total		30	

Grouping data

Counting travel destinations is an example of **discrete** data, which is always in whole numbers. Other data, such as ages of people or salaries paid, is **continuous** and can be any number. But for statistics we need to group the data. The data in the following table is part of a questionnaire enquiring about people's ages. Notice that the person designing the questionnaire has chosen to collect the ages in seven groups and has decided the boundaries for the groups.

Age in years	Less than 15 years	15–24	25–34	35–44	45–54	55–64	65 and above
Tally							

USEFUL KNOWLEDGE

Range
The range is the difference between the smallest number and the largest number in a set of a data.

Mean or arithmetic mean
The mean or simple average is a single number which gives a feeling for the centre of all numbers in a group. The mean is found by adding together all numbers in the data and dividing by how many numbers there are. The mean value is useful but can be misleading, so we might also use median or mode.

Median
For a set of data arranged in order of size, the median is the value of the middle of the set. For example, 7 is the median of 4, 4, 7, 9, 11.

Mode
The mode of a set of data is the value that is found most often. For example, 4 is the mode of 4, 4, 7, 9, 11.

Discrete data
Discrete data is obtained by counting and can only have fixed numbers. For example, the number of cars passing a point. There are no fractions.

Continuous data
Continuous data can be any size of number within agreed rules. For example, the figures for heights of people or weights of people can be any number, so we usually need to group them.

Measuring and observing

This chapter deals with ways of getting information by using equipment such as a watch or a thermometer. These instruments are used to **measure** how much we have of a **quantity** such as time or temperature. You can also obtain information about quantities by reading maps and technical drawings which have been drawn to scale.

Measuring systems

To measure a quantity such as time or length we have to agree upon a system of units. For example, seconds, minutes and hours is the system used by everyone to measure time. But for other measurements there has been a choice, such as metres or feet, degrees Celsius or degrees Fahrenheit.

The metric system, which uses units such as metres, grams and litres, is the official system of measurement in most countries. The metric system is also used for science and technology in all countries and is called the **SI system**. The **imperial system**, which uses units such as feet, pounds weight and gallons, is also in common use in the UK and the USA. Other sections of this book show you how to change between units, such as from degrees Celsius to degrees Fahrenheit.

Symbols

There is an official system of shorthand for writing units and these symbols are listed on page 23. Look at the following examples:

21 °C	means that the temperature is 21 degrees Celsius
1200 g	means that the mass is 1200 grams (sometimes grammes)
1.2 kg	means that the mass is 1.2 kilograms
3000 mm	means that the length is 3000 millimetres
3 m	means that the length is 3 metres

Large and small units

When the size of numbers in measurements gets large or small, we make the unit larger or smaller by putting a **prefix** word in front of the unit. For example, kilo always means one thousand (1000) and milli always means one-thousandth (1/1000).

Typical measurements
time
length
mass
volume
temperature

Some metric units
millimetre, metre, kilometre (for length)
gram, kilogram (for mass)
litre, cubic metre (for volume)
degree Celsius (for temperature)

Some imperial units
inch, foot (for length)
ounce, pound, stone (for mass)
pint, gallon, cubic feet (for volume)
degree Fahrenheit (for temperature)

See also: **Conversions**, page 32.

2 000 000 mm   is the same as 2000 m
2000 m   is the same as 2 km
2 km   is the same as 2 000 000 mm

The example shows how 2 kilometres can be written in at least three different ways. Although they all mean the same thing, we are more comfortable when handling smaller numbers. Therefore the general rule is that when there are more than four figures it is time to convert by using another prefix. So 2 000 000 mm needs converting to either 2000 m or to 2 km. Other prefixes are listed below.

1 kilovolt   = 1 kV = 1000 V
1 millimetre = 1 mm = 0.001 m

Quantity	Symbol	SI unit	Symbol
Some base units			
Length	*l*	metre	m
Mass	*m*	kilogram	kg
Time	*t*	second	s
Some other units			
Area	*A*	square metre	m^2
Volume	*V*	cubic metre	m^3
Velocity	*v*	metre per second	m/s
Force	*F*	newton	N
Energy	*E*	joule	J
Power	*P*	watt	W

Prefix	Symbol	Multiply by
mega	M	10^6 or 1 000 000
kilo	k	10^3 or 1000
		1
centi	c	10^{-2} or 0.01
milli	m	10^{-3} or 0.001
micro	μ	10^{-6} or 0.000 001

Notes
Centi is a non-standard prefix but remains because it is convenient.
Notice that M and m have different meanings.
The symbol μ is the Greek letter mu.

Reading scales

In most practical situations you use a ruler for measuring length, a set of scales for weighing mass, a thermometer for temperature, and so on. The scale that you read may be in a straight line or it may be a circular dial – the effect is the same.

When we look at the time on a clock face or measure with a ruler we often have to read *between* the markings and then decide what number it is and what units are being used. With a clock you have had many years of practice at judging where the hand is, and you know the units are hours and minutes. With some other measurements you need to take a little more care when reading the scale.

Oven temperature scale

Measuring jug

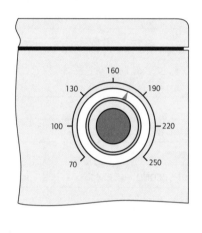

Kitchen scales

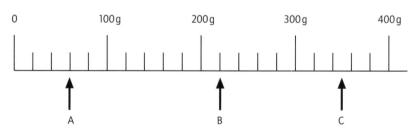

There are three points on the kitchen scales in the figure, marked A, B and C. To get a reading you need to use your eye to check the distance to the nearest marking on the scale. You then need to think about what number of grams that is. The scale is only marked every 100 g but there are five equal spaces between the markings. So each mark without a number is $\frac{1}{5}$ of 100 g which is 20 g.

Point	Reading	Working
A	60 g	Each marking is 20 g. Reading is 3 markings above 0 g. So add 3 × 20 g to 0, giving 60 g
B	220 g	Each marking is 20 g. Reading is 1 marking above 200 g. So add 1 × 20 g to 200 g, giving 220 g
C	350 g	Each marking is 20 g and this reading is halfway between 40 g and 60 g, i.e. 50 g. Then add 50 g to 300 g, giving 350 g

Maps and scales

When we make a map, a technical drawing or a model, it has to be smaller than the real thing otherwise we would need a piece of paper as big as the UK to make a map of the UK! But the reduction in size needs to have a fixed ratio or proportion which is called the **scale** of the map or drawing.

Example	Typical scale	Comment
Road map	1:500 000	1 cm on map is 500 000 cm of road (5000 m)
Technical drawing of a building	1:100	1 cm long on drawing is 100 cm (1 m) in building
Large model of a boat	1:20	1 inch on model is 20 inch of real boat

See also: **Ratio**, page 14.

Using maps

The scale of a map is marked somewhere on the map. It can be shown in the following ways:

A maths ratio   1:200 000
Metric units   2 km to 1 cm
Imperial units   3.2 miles to 1 inch
Measuring scale   A line in one corner of the map with marks to show typical real-world distances.

Here is an example of a measuring scale:

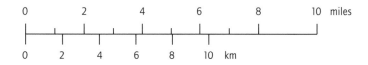

To use a map to find the distance in the real world:

- Measure a distance on the map.
- Use the scale to convert map distance to real distance.
- Write the units for the real distance.
- Check that the result is sensible.

If a map has a scale of 3.2 miles to 1 inch, then:
$\frac{1}{2}$ inch on the map will be $\frac{1}{2} \times 3.2 = 1.6$ real miles
2 inches on the map will be $2 \times 3.2 = 6.4$ real miles

> Roads on a map don't usually run in straight lines between places. So to measure a distance on the map you might use some cotton or string.

Using drawings

The scale of a technical drawing is marked somewhere on the drawing. It is usually shown as a maths ratio, e.g. 1:100, or as dimension lines. Dimension lines are lines with arrowheads to show the real-life distance between major points.

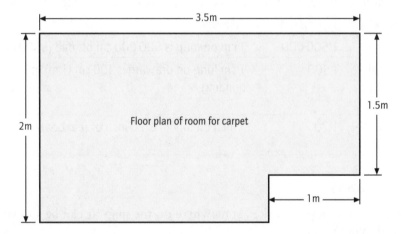

Floor plan of room for carpet

USEFUL KNOWLEDGE

SI metric units
The SI system is the official system of metric units based on the metre (m) for length, the kilogram (kg) for mass, and the second (s) for time.

1 cm = 10 mm	1 m = 100 cm	1 km = 1000 m
1 kg = 1000 g	1 tonne = 1000 kg	
1 litre = 1000 ml	1 litre = 1000 cm³	1 cm³ = 1 ml

Imperial units
Imperial units are based on the foot for length, the pound for mass, and the second for time. These systems are used in the UK and the USA and for some units, such as the gallon and the ton, the sizes are slightly different between the UK and the USA.

1 foot = 12 inches	1 yard = 3 feet
1 pound = 16 ounces (oz)	1 stone = 14 pounds (lb)
1 gallon = 8 pints	

Prefixes

A prefix is a group of letters in front of a word which modifies the meaning of the word. In the SI system, the prefix 'kilo' means multiply by 1000; examples are kilometre and kilovolt. See the table of SI units.

Rules for writing SI units

- Only one prefix can be used, so kilokilovolt becomes megavolt.
- Numbers are expressed in groups of three; they are separated by spaces not commas, e.g. 3 000 000.
- Units start with a lower case letter when written in full but their abbreviations begin with a capital letter. The newton (N) is the unit for measuring force and the pascal (Pa) is the unit for measuring pressure.

Rules for using scales

- Measure a distance on the map or drawing.
- Use the scale to convert paper distance to real distance.
- Add units for the real distance.
- Check that the result is sensible.

The Learning Curve

059478

MEASURING AND OBSERVING | **27**

Calculations

We all do calculations in our lives, even if it is to decide when and how long to watch TV! These additions and subtractions of numbers are part of arithmetic and this chapter reminds you about correct terms and rules to use. It then leads on to the idea of using formulas for doing calculations.

Calculators

Remember 'gigo': garbage in, garbage out.

Simple electronic calculators are found everywhere and we can use them to do the hard boring crunch of calculations. But *you* still need to do the thinking because the calculator does exactly what it is told, for good or bad. For example, did we enter the correct numbers and does the final answer seem sensible?

Calculators come in various types; they include simple calculators, scientific calculators, programmable calculators and graphics calculators. This book concentrates on the use of the simple calculator like the one illustrated here. If you do have a more advanced model, make sure you don't get confused by the extra keys. Learn to use them by reading the instructions. All types of calculator are used in three stages:

1. Entering numbers
2. Entering operations
3. Reading the result

Calculator operations

Operations are what a calculator does with numbers when you press the instruction buttons, such as the ADD button. To add the numbers, 34, 19 and 27.5, press the following keys:

For a definition of square root, *see* **Useful Knowledge**, page 36.

and the calculator display should show the answer:

The last answer needs no change as it is already correct to 1 decimal place. But try a calculation like dividing 20 by 3:

and the display will show this:

Because of the repeating number, the calculator has given an answer that is more accurate than you need. Decide how many decimal places you need then use the rules of rounding explained in previous sections. If you decide to use 2 decimal places, you could write your answer as 6.67 (2 dp).

Common errors with calculators
Not clearing old numbers on screen.
Entering wrong numbers.
Not pressing = at the end.

> **Take care!** A computer keyboard has a calculator keypad. The key for multiply is often marked with a *. The symbols * and × mean the same thing – multiply. The key for divide is often marked with a /. The symbols / and ÷ mean the same thing – divide.

Here are some of the other calculator buttons.

Button	Operation	Effect
+	Addition	Adds
−	Subtraction	Subtracts (takes away)
×	Multiplication	Multiplies (times)
÷	Division	Divides
C/CE or CLR	Clear	Clears display and clears memories
M+	Memory in +	Stores number and/or adds it to anything in memory
M−	Memory in −	Stores number and/or subtracts it from anything in memory
MR or RCL	Memory out	Recalls number from memory and onto display, where it can be used
√	Square root	Works out square root
%	Percentage	Adds or subtracts a percentage change

Checking calculations

All calculations are a waste of time if you get results which don't make sense or have no use. Use the following questions and checks to help you get meaningful results.

Check	Examples
Is the input data correct?	Read the instrument correctly Check the scales and units Copy or write the numbers down correctly.
Is the formula correct?	Choose the right formula Write it down correctly Put the right figures in the formula
Have I used the calculator correctly?	Use the correct keys Copy correctly from the screen
Can I get the same result twice?	Repeat the above stages
Does the result agree with an estimated result?	Estimate by rounding the figures to 1 or 2 significant figures and do a simple sum
Is the accuracy suitable?	The calculator may read 21.472 38 but you only need 4 significant figures
Do I need to use units?	The final answer might be in metres or degrees

Order of operations

When a calculation has several types of operation, such as addition mixed with multiplication, then we need to take care. Calculations need to be done in the correct order, otherwise they are wrong. For example, if you work out the following calculation then you can get two different answers:

$4 + 3 \times 2 = 14$ $\times$

$4 + 3 \times 2 = 10$ $\checkmark$

The correct answer of 10 is obtained by doing the multiplication first to give 6, and then adding 4. Multiplication has priority over addition and the general rule is as follows:

> *Multiplication* and *division* must be done **before** *addition* and *subtraction*

Some calculators are clever enough to help you with this rule, but once again *you* need to be in control. To check the effect of your calculator keys, use simple figures for which you already know the answer, like those in the example.

The Learning Curve

Brackets

LEVEL 2

Brackets are the curved signs which can be put around words (like this) and around maths (3×2). If you start with an opening bracket, you always need to finish with a closing bracket. If you start with (you must finish with). Brackets can be used to help people calculate things in the right order. If the previous example is written as

$4 + (3 \times 2) =$

then the brackets are a signal to multiply 3×2 first and then add 4. It never hurts to use brackets if it helps make the calculation clearer. So the final operation is

$4 + 6 =$

A simple calculator doesn't usually have keys for brackets, so you may need to write down an intermediate stage such as the result of 3×2. Or you can learn to use the memory keys on your calculator.

BODMAS

There is a rule that gives the correct order for doing all calculations and for writing down formulas. The strange-sounding word BODMAS is made up from letters of the following operations starting with B for brackets:

First do	Brackets	so $4 + (3 \times 2)$ is $4 + 6$
Then do	Other (or power)	such as 3^2 or $\sqrt{4}$

| Then do | Divide or Multiply |
| Then do | Add or Subtract |

If there are no brackets, or powers, then just move to the next calculation in the list. It doesn't actually matter in which order you divide or multiply as they have equal priority but both of them have a higher priority than add and subtract.

Conversions

In an earlier section of the book we used a graph to convert between the temperature units of degrees Celsius and degrees Fahrenheit. If you don't have a graph, you can use a formula. The simplest type of formula is to multiply by a **conversion factor** such as those listed in the table. (The conversion factors are given to 2 significant figures).

Imperial units into metric units			Metric units to imperial units		
To convert	into	multiply by	To convert	into	multiply by
inches	centimetres	2.5	centimetres	inches	0.39
feet	metres	0.30	metres	feet	3.3
yards	metres	0.91	metres	yards	1.1
miles	kilometres	1.6	kilometres	miles	0.62
sq yards	sq metres	0.84	sq metres	sq yards	1.2
cubic feet	cubic metres	0.028	cubic metres	cubic feet	35
gallons	litres	4.5	litres	gallons	0.22
pounds	kilograms	0.45	kilograms	pounds	2.2
ounces	grams	28	grams	ounces	0.04

Conversion factors are numbers used to multiply one unit to convert it to an equivalent amount in another unit. The units might be measurements such as length; the conversion factor never changes. Or the units might be for money, in which case you have to look up the latest exchange rate.

Convert a length of 8 inches to centimetres; work to 2 significant figures.

Steps	Working
Write down inches	8 inches
Look up table of conversion factors	multiply inches by 2.5
Calculate	$8 \times 2.5 = 20$
Interpret result	8 in converts to 20 cm (2 sf)

Formulas

Instructions to carry out calculations can be written entirely in words such as:

the area of a rectangle equals the length times the width

We might then shorten the words to:

Area = length × width

The next step in the shorthand is to simply write:

$A = l \times w$

The numbers you multiply depend upon the size of your particular rectangle, such as a room, but this general **formula** works for any length or width. Using letters to stand in for numbers is called **algebra** and its ideas can become very powerful. For key skills we only need to use the shorthand of algebra in order to get results.

Using formulas

To use a general formula like those for areas and volumes, you need to have certain measurements available, such as the length and width of a room. The method of putting real numbers into a formula is called **substitution**. Just like substituting players in a football team, the aim is keep the same balance in the formula.

Shorthand in formulas
lw means $l \times w$
d/t or $\frac{d}{t}$ means $d \div t$

A room is measured and found to be 3 metres long by 2.5 metres wide. The following steps of working show how to calculate the area of the room using the formula $A = l \times w$.

Steps	Working
Interpret the information Write down what you know and don't know	$A = ?$ $l = 3$ m $w = 2.5$ m
Write down the formula	$A = l \times w$ ($A = lw$ if you prefer to omit ×)
Substitute what you know into the formula	$A = 3 \times 2.5$
Carry out the calculation	$A = 7.5$
Interpret and present the results Put the answer back into words and add units	Area is 7.5 square metres .

Formulae is an alternative spelling for formulas.

The next figure gives formulas for the areas, volumes and other dimensions of common shapes. Using some of these formulas can get tricky and you are best to write out all lines of working, as above.

Rectangle

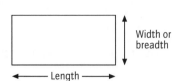

Area = length × width
Perimeter = 2 × (length + width)

Parallelogram

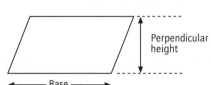

Area = base × perpendicular height

Triangle

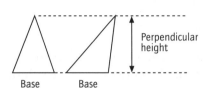

Area = $\frac{1}{2}$ × base × perpendicular height

Circle

Area = π × radius × radius = πr^2 or $\frac{1}{4}\pi d^2$
Circumference = 2 × π × radius
$\qquad\qquad$ = π × diameter = πd

Arc of a circle

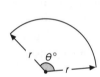

Length of arc = $\dfrac{\text{Angle (in degrees) of arc at centre}}{360}$ × circumference of full circle

$\qquad\qquad = \dfrac{\theta°}{360°} = 2\pi r^2$

Section of a circle

Area of sector = angle (in degrees) of sector at centre × area of full circle

$\qquad\qquad = \dfrac{\theta°}{360°} \times \pi r^2$

Cylinder

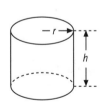

Volume = π × radius × radius × height = $\pi r^2 h$
Curved surface area = 2 × π × radius × height
$\qquad\qquad\qquad\quad = 2\pi rh$
Total surface area $\quad = 2\pi r (r + h)$

Cone

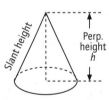

Volume = $\frac{1}{3}$ × area of base × perpendicular height
$\qquad\quad = \frac{1}{3} \pi r^2 h$
Curved surface area
$\qquad\quad$ = π × radius of base × slant height
Slant height = $\sqrt{r^2 + h^2}$

Sphere

Volume $= \frac{3}{4} \times \pi \times (\text{radius})^3 = \frac{1}{6} \pi \times (\text{diameter})^3$

Surface area $= 4 \times \pi \times (\text{radius})^2 = \pi \times (\text{diameter})^2$

Pyramid

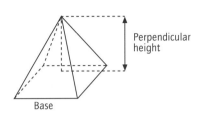

Perpendicular height

Base

Volume $= \frac{1}{3} \times$ area of base $\times$ perpendicular height

The formula to calculate the area of a rectangle, $A = lw$, uses only two **variables** (things that can change) and only one **operation** (multiply). But some formulas contain rather more variables and have a sequence of operations. Always follow BODMAS when creating or using a formula. Here are some examples.

Formula	Used for	Notes
$V = IR$	Voltage (V) when given the electric current (I) and the resistance (R)	This if the formula which results from Ohm's law in science
$I = \frac{PR}{100}$	Simple interest for one year, where P is the loan (principal) and R is the interest rate	Calculate in any order
$A = \pi r^2$	Area of a circle, where r is the radius	First calculate the square of r then multiply by the constant π
$A = 2\pi (r + h)$	Total surface area of a cylinder, where r is the radius and h is the height	First calculate $(r + h)$ then multiply by 2π
$C = \frac{5}{9} (F - 32)$	To convert degrees Fahrenheit (F) to degrees Celsius (C)	First calculate $(F - 32)$ then multiply by $\frac{5}{9}$
$F = \frac{9}{5} C + 32$	To convert degrees Celsius (C) to degrees Fahrenheit (F)	First calculate $\frac{9}{5} C$ then add 32

Square

To square a number is to multiply that number by itself.

Symbol: N^2 where N is the number you are squaring

Example: 4^2 means work out $4 \times 4 = 16$

Square root

When you multiply a number by itself you obtain a square – 16 is the square of 4.

The number that you multiplied by itself is the square root – 4 is the square root of 16.

Symbol: $\sqrt{N}$ where N is the number you are taking the square root of

Example: $\sqrt{36} = 6$ (because $6 \times 6 = 36$)

BODMAS rule

brackets first then other (such as powers), then divide and multiply, then add and subtract.

Algebra

The branch of maths which deals with calculations by using general letters or symbols to represent numbers.

Shorthand in formulas

ab means a multiplied by b

a/b or $\frac{a}{b}$ means a divided by b

Part 2: The Bottom Line

This part concentrates on what you must do to get your key skills qualification. It will show you:

- The words and ideas of the key skills.
- The difference between level 1 and level 2.
- How you can practise the skills.
- What must be in your portfolio of evidence.

This part is divided into four sections:

- **What the unit expects**: This section will explain the evidence requirements of the number key skill, and how to put your portfolio together. Your portfolio is the key to getting your key skill – this part of the book tells you how to choose your evidence and get it ready.
- **Evidence for level 1**
- **Evidence for level 2**
- **Other forms of assessment and evidence**: This section will tell you about the external assessment and how to prepare for it.

Qualifications and Curriculum Authority

The key skills specifications are published by the QCA, and are widely available through schools, colleges, training establishments and awarding bodies. They are also available on the QCA website (www.qca.org.uk).

What the unit expects

What's the difference between levels 1 and 2?

Evidence is the proof that you can do what is required in order to get the key skill. It is proof that you have learned about number and that you can use and apply what you have learned.

You need to be clear about what level of number key skill you intend to collect evidence for. This may depend on the GNVQ you are taking; for foundation GNVQ the appropriate choice is level 1 number, for intermediate GNVQ an appropriate choice is level 2 number. For GSCE equivalents, remember that level 1 is roughly the same as D–F and level 2 is roughly A–C. If you are able to, you can try to achieve a higher-level key skill. However, it is always a good idea to make sure that you at least achieve the key skill appropriate to the other qualifications you are taking.

What is level 1 all about?

At level 1 you will see there are basically three types of **evidence** that you need to provide. The key skill unit at level 1 asks you to show that you can apply your number skills and provide evidence for the following three areas:

- Interpreting information using numbers
- Carrying out calculations
- Interpreting results and presenting findings

You can collect the evidence for each of the three areas from different places if you like. For example, one GNVQ unit or GCSE or another qualification might be great for showing that you can interpret information but might not be much use at helping you collect evidence to show you can carry out calculations. Another opportunity might exist for only carrying out calculations and nothing else. At level 1 this doesn't matter and, whenever you can, you should make use of your best opportunities for collecting evidence.

How is level 2 different?

You will need to provide different types of evidence for Application of Number at level 2, the intermediate level. Level 2 is a harder level to achieve and it will involve showing two things:

- You can work at a harder level.
- You can work successfully using different types of numbers and number techniques.

The first point to note is that some of the evidence requirements are different and that you will need to show you can work with more difficult sources of number information, be able to cope with more difficult calculations and do more when presenting.

You will also have to show that you are able to provide evidence for at least one task involving interpreting information and carrying out calculations. You then go on to interpret the results and present the findings from your work. In other words, you must do at least one task that involves all three stages of the key skill together. So you will need to have a purpose that will allow you to do this.

What's your point?

It is not enough to just interpret or present information that uses numbers. You need to have a **purpose** for using the numbers you collect. The number key skill will keep asking you to use the numbers for a purpose and you will need to provide evidence that you have a purpose in mind and you can use the information effectively to meet it. Finding out when the next train leaves, wanting to find out how much you have in the bank, trying to find out how much carpet to buy or even using a thermometer to find out the temperature, all are reasons or purposes for using numbers.

The Bottom Line

SOURCES THAT USE NUMBERS

At levels 1 and level 2 you need to show you can use at least **two** different sources of information. However, each level has slightly different requirements. Look at the information below to help you understand what you need to do.

At level 1 you must show you can use at least **one** of the following: table (currency, temperature), diagram, chart, line graph

At level 2 you must show you can use a graph as one of your sources.

Then you can choose any other sources.

Plus one of the sources of information not already used. For example, at level 1, if you are using a table you could also use a chart or a diagram or line graph. At level 2 you could use diagrams, charts or tables as well as the graph. You could also use examples from the list below:

Thermometer
Scales
Other measuring instruments, e.g. a micrometer
Electricity and/or gas meters
Map, when using the scale to measure distances between places
Bank statements
Bills
Payslips
Petrol pumps for amount of petrol drawn, price per litre and amount spent
Car dials and tripometers
Scale drawings
Schematic drawings
Floor plans and building drawings

What about your portfolio?

Building your portfolio of Application of Number evidence

Your portfolio of evidence is the work that you have done to prove to your teacher and others that you can do what the key skill asks you to do.

The simplest approach to collecting and keeping your evidence is to have a separate folder or portfolio for your number evidence. This is by far the easiest way to organise your work and keep a record of what you have done and what there is still to do. Consider using the following handy references as a way of organising and labelling your work:

- Have a contents page that you keep updating as you build up your evidence.
- Keep records of when you collected your evidence and where it came from (e.g. which GCSE or GNVQ unit).
- Get into the habit of writing down the purpose for your work as you collect evidence.
- Use the key skill sections (interpreting information, calculating and presenting your findings) as sections dividing up your portfolio.
- Copies of work are acceptable if the actual key skill evidence is part of another course; the original work can be kept with the course that it comes from.
- Keep a checklist of all the things that you must cover in your portfolio (in the presenting section you must show you can use one chart and one diagram).

A key skill unit is quite a large chunk of work. It is roughly the same size as a GNVQ unit and just a little smaller than a GCSE. So you may have to carry out a number of different tasks to have sufficient evidence to show you can meet the key skill requirements.

Evidence for level 1

At level 1 the important word is **straightforward**. The key skill specifications use the word 'straightforward' to show the difference between level 1 and level 2. It is used to indicate the different degrees of difficulty between levels 1 and 2. You need to show that you can perform straightforward tasks, working with straightforward information to carry out straightforward calculations.

What is straightforward information?

Straightforward information is information that you should come across regularly at school or college, at work or in other activities. It's the type of numbers that you might have to deal with in everyday life. It is worthwhile thinking about all the different numbers you have to deal with every single day. Each of these everyday activities provides an opportunity to use numbers:

- Dealing with money
- Understanding bills
- Shopping and working out discounts
- Measuring

What are straightforward calculations?

Straightforward calculations involve working out answers to basic problems involving numbers. They should be about showing you can cope with everyday types of situations where you need to use numbers for working out areas or volumes, working out distances, calculating percentages or even calculating the average in a range of numbers.

Interpreting information

What you must learn to do

- **Read and understand straightforward tables, charts, diagrams and line graphs.** You should be looking for opportunities that will show you can understand bar charts, pie charts and straightforward tables like train timetables, tables with prices in a holiday brochure or

sports league tables. Examples of line graphs that would be appropriate to use at this level include graphs showing temperature readings.

- **Read and understand the same number expressed in different ways.** Concentrate on learning about and being able to show you can use the following types of numbers.

Number type	Examples
Large numbers	Five hundred and seventy-two (572)
	Three thousand five hundred (3500)
	Seventy-eight thousand nine hundred and sixty-seven (78 967)
Simple fractions	$\frac{1}{2}, \frac{3}{4}$
Decimals	0.25, 3.51, 10.87 (2 dp)
Percentages	20%, 33%, 50%, 66%, 75%

- **Measure in everyday units.** If you are measuring things, you will need to show you can use everyday units of measurement like hours and minutes using a watch (time), litres using a measuring jug (volume of fluids), kilograms and grams using weighing scales (weight) and degrees Celsius using a thermometer (temperature).

- **Make accurate observations.** This involves showing that you can interpret the number information you need correctly and read sources of the information accurately. You will also need to show that you can collect information accurately; for example, when you count numbers of people during a survey.

- **Identify suitable calculations to get the results that you need.**

Collecting evidence

All examples are suggestions that you could try as a way of practising. There is not enough space to put in proper explanations of the methods suggested or to justify what is suggested. You will have to do this when you generate your evidence for real.

HOW TO GET YOUR EVIDENCE

What you need to do	Using currency	Using train times
Get information you need by looking at different sources of numbers.	You want to show the relationship between different currencies, e.g. the pound (£) and the US dollar ($).	You want to find out how long you have to wait until the next train to Manchester and then calculate how long it is going to take to get there once the train leaves your station.
You will need to show you can use at least two different sources of information. At least one must be a table, chart, diagram or line graph.	**Sources:** look in a newspaper to find the tables showing currency exchange rates.	**Sources:** train timetable (table) and a watch.
Then sort out which calculations you will use to get the results you need.	**Calculations:** Multiplication (which will involve decimals) to work out different currency train values.	**Calculations:** subtraction using timetable to get the departure time and your watch to work out how long you have to wait.
		Subtraction using the timetable probably using the 24-hour clock to establish the length of the train trip.
		You could check your subtractions by using the 'adding back' method.

Evidence requirements in a nutshell

You need to find out information for a reason (this is your purpose). You need to show you can use two different types of number information in order to get this part of the key skill. One of the types of number information has got to be a table, a chart, a diagram or a line graph. The other source of information could be a different one from these four or a completely different source of information.

You must also write down any of the calculations you will need to do to get the information you are looking for.

Hints for interpreting information at level 1

- **State your purpose.** Write down clearly what you are trying to do and why you need the number information you are collecting.
- **Save your proof.** Keep a copy of all the sources of information you use.

Carrying out calculations

What you must learn to do

- **Work to the level of accuracy that you have been told.** For example, working to the nearest whole number, nearest 10 or to two decimal places. If you are reading maps or working in distances it could even be to the nearest mile or kilometre. If you are wondering why bother rounding numbers, well it is because it makes calculating more simple and straightforward, allowing you to quickly check your answers in your head.

- **Add, subtract, multiply and divide with whole numbers and simple decimals (e.g. to 2 dp).**

- **Understand and find simple fractions and percentages and use ratios and proportions.** This should be based on straightforward calculations like working out $\frac{3}{4}$ of £10, $\frac{2}{3}$ of £21 and percentages like 25% of 400 and 66% of 600. You should also be able to recognise that 25% of something is also the same as a quarter ($\frac{1}{4}$) and 33% is roughly a third ($\frac{1}{3}$) if you are working to the nearest whole number. Ratios and proportions are like working with fractions. You need to know about sizes of one thing in relation to another (e.g. something is three times the size).

- **Work out areas of rectangular shapes and volumes of simple spaces with a rectangular base.** Examples could include the area of a floor or a sports field. You need to show that you can work out the area by multiplying the length by the width. For volumes you need to show that you can calculate the volume of an object by multiplying the length by the width by the depth.

- **Use straightforward scales on diagrams.** You will get opportunities to show that you know how to do this when you work with maps, scale drawings or plans.

- **Find the range for up to 10 items.** This involves taking up to 10 measurements or readings from an instrument and showing that you can work out the range from the highest reading to the lowest reading.

- **Check your calculations.** This involves showing that, when needed, you can double-check your calculations by using another way of working out the answer.

Rounding to the nearest 10: Round down from numbers under 5 and up from numbers 5 and up.

Rounding to the nearest 100: Round down to the nearest 100 by rounding down from 49 or less and up from 50 and up.

Rounding to the nearest 1000: Round down to the nearest 1000 from 499 or less and up from 500 and up.

Area: Working out an area involves two measurements (length × width); the answer is a size squared (e.g. cm² or m²). Think of the number 2.

Volume: Working out a volume involves three measurements (length × width × breadth); the answer is a size cube (e.g. cm³ or m³). Think of the number 3.

Collecting evidence

What you need to do	Using amounts and sizes	Working with statistics
Do calculations that will mean working with these three things: amounts and sizes, scales and proportions, statistics. Check with your teacher what the levels of accuracy are that you must work to. Then make sure that your answers are correct or as accurate as they should be.	Calculate the cost of buying a carpet for a room that is 11 metres by 7 metres. The cost of the carpet is £5.60 a square metre. Round your answer to the nearest £1. Calculate the area of the room in square metres ($11 \times 7 = 77$ m^2). Multiply the area of the room by the cost of the carpet ($77 \times 5.60 = £431.20$). Check your answer. Round off the answer to £431.	Find out the average noon temperature for one week. Take 7 noon temperature measurements, one for each day of the week. This is working with a range of up to 10 items. Then work out the average temperature.

Evidence requirements in a nutshell

First of all find out what the level of accuracy is that you must work to. The level of accuracy will depend on what it is you are doing, so establish what it is before you start. Once you know how accurate you have to be, then start doing your calculations. Once you have finished your calculations, find out how you could check your work. Check it, including checking that you are accurate enough.

> *Hints for carrying out calculations at level 1*
>
> - Write down the expected level of accuracy as part of your work.
> - Keep this written record as part of your evidence.
> - Have three separate records that show your calculations on (a) amounts and sizes, (b) scales and proportion, (c) statistics.
> - Make sure you check and then double-check your answers.
> - Keep records of how you checked your work.

Interpreting results and presenting your findings

What you must learn to do

If you have gone to a lot of trouble to calculate information from different sources, it would be a shame not to present your work clearly and in

a way that people can understand. Communicating your results is important and one useful way that can be easily understood is to present them graphically (using charts and diagrams). You must show you can:

- Use suitable ways of presenting information, including a chart and diagram.
- Use the correct units for measurements of quantities like area, volume, weight, time and temperature.
- Label your work accurately using appropriate titles for any axes used in your graphs, any rows and columns in your tables, or keys if you need them. You must also choose an appropriate title for the whole graph, table or chart – a total that describes what it shows.
- Explain why your calculation work met the purpose of your task.

Collecting evidence

HOW TO GET YOUR EVIDENCE

What you need to do	Using charts	Using diagrams
Write out what the answers from your calculations mean. Your answers are your findings Find good ways of presenting the findings and present them clearly.	If you have taken a range of temperature measurements, turn you measurements into a graph.	I have 30 books at home, 20 are fiction and 10 are non-fiction. I have worked out what each type of book represents as a percentage of the total and what the ratio of one is to another.
Explain why you think the ways you have chosen to present your results are effective and appropriate. Make sure you use one chart and one diagram in this part of your portfolio.	Start with the range of temperatures written up as a table. Make sure you have a brief description of what you have done and how you got the answers.	I am going to find an unusual and interesting way to present this information.
	A bar chart is a good way of presenting the data simply and clearly. However, you might need to choose an appropriate scale that will help show differences in temperature more clearly. If this is the case then you should have a note describing this. Label clearly.	I am going to represent the two totals on a pictogram using pictures of books.
Describe how your results help you with the purpose of your task.		I am also going to draw a book outline and shade in an appropriate amount to represent the number of fiction and the number of non-fiction.
	Provide a note explaining how the results relate to your original purpose.	I will need to label this diagram clearly to make sure people can follow the information.

Evidence requirements in a nutshell

In this section you need to show that you can create your own graphical information, like diagrams and charts based on information you have collected. Being clear about what your calculations mean will help you when it comes to labelling your work, i.e. putting titles on any graphs or diagrams. Think about the best ways to present your information. Consider how to make your information easier for other people to understand. Make sure you are writing down your thoughts on the methods you use and why. Also record the methods that you rejected and why you rejected them.

Present your information using your chosen methods. Make sure your work is clear. Then provide a brief explanation to say how everything meets your purpose – your calculations and the results you have presented.

Hints for interpreting results and presenting your findings at level 1

- Make sure each of your charts and diagrams has clear labels and a title that explains what it shows.
- Make sure you have used the correct units of measurement for whatever you measure.

Evidence for level 2

Information

At level 2 you need to show you can use a range of different sources and take relevant information from them to help you fulfil your purpose. This can involve secondary sources with both written and graphical material, but you must also learn how to generate your own information by using primary sources, creating your information first-hand. Taking measurements, carrying out surveys and making observations are three examples of activities you could do to create information.

Calculations

Calculations at level 2 must involve two or more steps. This is to make sure the calculations you do at level 2 are harder than the straightforward calculations expected at level 1.

Two or more steps just means that you have to take at least two steps or two stages of working out before you get the answer. If you are calculating the area of a circle that has a radius of 3 cm, using the formula πr^2, then the steps will look like this:

Why squared? Well, if you look at this example, 3 squared equals 9, the number 9 is known as a square number because it is the area of a square with side length 3.

- **Step 1:** substitute in the values using 3.14, which is π to 2 decimal places:
$$\pi r^2 = 3.14 \times 3^2$$
- **Step 2:** work out the value of 3 squared then multiply by 3.14:
$$3^2 = 9$$
$$3.14 \times 9 = 28.26 \text{ cm}^2$$
- **Answer:** the area of the circle is 28.26 cm^2.

At level 2 you also need to show you can handle and compare large sets of data. At this level a large set means at least 20 items. Such a large data set will allow you to show that you can make comparisons and even identify the different types of averages that are present.

> **Take care!** One more key feature of the level 2 number requirements is that you must to do at least one task that involves interpreting information, carrying out calculations and interpreting results and presenting your findings, all as part of the same task.

The rest of the evidence can be done by taking each of the three areas individually, doing different tasks for each or by putting together evidence that involves two of the areas, if this is appropriate. Because of the amount of evidence you will need to produce, you will probably use all three ways of generating evidence.

Interpreting information

What you must learn to do

- **Work with graphs, tables, charts and diagrams.** At level 2 the types of example you should be capable of understanding include pie charts, frequency diagrams, stack graphs, graphs involving negative numbers, line graphs, graphs showing more than one variable as well as bar charts and other simpler forms of graphs and charts.

- **Work with numbers used in different ways, including negative numbers.** Here are some examples of negative numbers used in different ways:
  1. Temperatures that drop below zero when you measure in degrees Celsius.
  2. Bank statements, credit card statements or other financial records that show accounts in debit (in the red). If you are looking at company charts or graphs that show shares or other financial information like losses in trading, then you will sometimes be dealing with negative numbers.
  3. Graphs can often be used to show negative numbers as well as positive numbers. Normally the *y*-axis puts zero at its centre then measures positive numbers up the page and negative numbers down the page. If you were creating a bar chart, you would then draw the bars up or down depending on the number you were showing.

- **Estimate amounts and proportions.** This skill is useful for two reasons:
  1. You can quickly read and interpret information without getting too involved in the detail. However, you need to be careful and establish what degree of accuracy you need to work to before you decide how you start estimating.
  2. It is also useful as a way of checking that your answers look correct. This involves doing a quick calculation, often in your head, to make sure the answer you got using another method (say by using a calculator) looks right. The following table is an example of some figures you might total by calculator then check by mental addition. If you were doing the calculation in your head and rounding off the numbers to the nearest 50p, you would expect the total to be about £10.

Actual price	Rounded amount
£3.47	£3.50
£0.89	£1.00
£4.36	£4.50
£1.17	£1
£9.89 (actual total)	£10 (estimated total)

- **Work with scales on a range of equipment to given levels of accuracy.** This shows that you are able to collect your own information or data by being able to use different types of equipment. You must also learn how to identify what is the appropriate level of accuracy to use when taking readings from the equipment. This will normally depend on two things:
  1. The type of equipment and its levels of accuracy
  2. The type of task you are doing
  Each might influence the level of accuracy that you need to work to. It is always important to note down your level of accuracy when you are using equipment and explain why you are using this level of accuracy. This will help others to understand your work. For example, if you are measuring the area of a field and need to take the length and width of the field, you might decide that taking the size to the nearest metre is accurate enough. The nearest centimetre might be more accurate than you need, so it would be an unnecessary level of detail.

- **Taking accurate observations.** When you don't use equipment to generate your own number information and you use other methods instead, for example, observing the number of customers who buy something in a one-hour period, you still need to show that you can be accurate in your work. This means it is important to show how you tried to keep your number or data collecting accurate when you were generating your figures.

- **Deciding on appropriate methods for collecting data and results.** Here you need to show that besides collecting information accurately you can also choose the best way to do it. It helps if you write down a note to explain to others why you chose to use the methods you used. It can be something as simple as deciding to use equipment a bit more appropriate than a 30 cm ruler to measure the length of a field; or something more complicated, like show that the best way to group data from a survey was to put people into different age categories.

Collecting evidence

All examples are suggestions that you could try as a way of practising. There is not enough space to put in proper explanations of the methods suggested or justify what is suggested. You will have to do this when you generate your evidence for real.

HOW TO GET YOUR EVIDENCE

What you need to do	Currency conversion	Tiling a bathroom
What is your purpose? How are you going to get the information you need in order to meet your purpose? Get the information you need. You will need to show you can use at least two different sources in total. One of the sources of information you use at some point must contain a graph. Use appropriate methods to get the results you need from the information you have collected.	I want to find out how many US dollars ($) I can get for £50. I am going to look in today's paper to find out the value of the pound (£) against the US dollar ($). I can find this in newspapers that have money or travel sections. Once I have this information I will use my calculator to multiply it by 59 to get the value of £50. I can check my answer in my head by multiplying the value of £1's worth of dollars by 100, rounding the answer off and then dividing it by 2 to get £50. This is a useful way of checking that I have used the calculator correctly, because the numbers should be roughly the same. I will then round my answer to the nearest 50p.	I want to find out the area of the walls and ceiling in a bathroom to work out the cost of tiling it. I have prices of different kinds of tile and I also want to differences in cost of using different tiles. If there is one available, I could use a scale drawing or I can take measurements. I need to be able to calculate the area of the window and the door and make appropriate deductions. They won't need tiles! The scale on the drawing will help me get the real sizes or a tape measure would be appropriate equipment to use. *Continued on page 54*

Evidence requirements in a nutshell

You need to have a purpose for gathering the number information. Then you need to sort out how you will get hold of this information. Having done this, you need to get the information and work out how you are going to get the results you need using appropriate ways of doing this (your methods). You must have evidence to show you can use at least two different sources of number information. Make sure that you will get some of your information for one of the activities that will eventually become evidence in your portfolio from reading a graph.

Hints for interpreting information at level 2

- Keep a written record of what your purpose is.
- Keep a written record of how or where you found the sources of information.
- Keep copies of your different sources.
- Keep a copy of the graph that you have used and the information you got from it.

The Bottom Line

Carrying out calculations

What you must learn to do

- **Convert between fractions, decimals and percentages.** Sometimes you might prefer to use fractions because they are more exact and accurate. For example, we have used $\pi = 3.14$ (2 dp). It is more accurately expressed as $\frac{22}{7}$. See π more accurately expressed by dividing 22 by 7 on your calculator. Even then it is still only to a certain number of decimal places; π goes on and on past this. More common is using $\frac{1}{3}$ as a more accurate way of saying 33.33333% or $\frac{2}{3}$ instead of 66.6%. You will need to use your skills to represent numbers to show you know what would be an appropriate way to present them to communicate your work more effectively.

Conversions	Simple Rules	Examples
Decimals to percentages	Move the decimal point two places to the right and add a % sign.	$0.73 = 73\%$ $0.0021 = 0.21\%$
Percentages to decimals	Drop the % sign and move the decimal point two places to the left.	$75\% = 0.75$
Percentages to fractions	Drop the % sign and use a denominator of 100. Then reduce the fraction you get to its lowest terms.	$28\% = \frac{28}{100}$ $= \frac{14}{50} = \frac{7}{25}$
Fractions to percentages	Write the fraction as a decimal and then change to a percentage following the rules above. Or if you can, rewrite the fraction with a denominator of 100, drop the 100 and add a % sign.	$\frac{3}{4} = 0.75 = 75\%$ or $\frac{9}{10} = \frac{90}{100} = 90\%$
Fractions to decimals	Divide the numerator by the denominator.	$\frac{5}{8} = 5$ divided by 8 $= 0.625$

- **Convert between different number measurement systems.** There are several different measurement systems you could use to show that you can make conversions. You could look at converting between the following:
  1. Metric to imperial systems (e.g. kilograms to pounds, grams to ounces, metres to feet and years, centimetres to inches).

2. Temperatures in degrees Celsius to temperatures in degrees Fahrenheit.
3. From the pound (£) to any foreign currency, even the euro (€).
4. The 24-hour clock to the 12-hour clock.

- **Calculate areas and volumes.** Make sure your area and volume calculations are appropriate to this level. You need to be doing more complicated calculations than just the area of a rectangular shape. Look for appropriate opportunities to show that you can taken an area of a more complicated shape by breaking it down into regular shapes and adding the results. For example, if you had to take the area of an L-shaped room, then the L-shape could be seen as two rectangles. You could then take the area of each rectangle and add them together. Here are some examples that indicate what is appropriate.

Areas	Volumes
The floor area of a rectangular room that needs to be carpeted but has a rectangular fire-lace in it, which doesn't need carpeting. So area of room minus area of fireplace.	Volume of a cube
The area of an arch window. An arch window is just a rectangle with half a circle on top. So half the area of a circle added to the area of rectangle.	Volume of cylinder
The surface area of a simple stairway. The stairway is lots of rectangles added together. Remember the steps themselves and the vertical area between each step.	Working out calculations that combine volumes. For example, how many cans (a can is a cylinder) would fit into a box (a box is rectangular-based space)

- **Calculate dimensions from scale drawings.** It doesn't matter if you are going to use a map, a plan of a building or a scale drawing of a large object like a plane, a ship or a skyscraper. You need to show that you can work with scales and that you can calculate the actual size of what is shown by using the scale given.

- **Work with proportions and calculate using ratios where appropriate.** You may find that expressing information in proportions or ratios is the most appropriate or simplest way to get your point across. In certain circumstances it is easier to understand something compared to something else as a ratio or proportion. This is especially the case with mixtures, different quantities or when dealing with probability (especially the likelihood of winning something).

Remember **BODMAS**, page 31.

- **Work with sets of data having a minimum of 20 items.** This is your opportunity to show you can calculate and use types of averages (mean, median and mode) when you analyse your data. You can also show the range of the data. This is really about communicating to others the size or extent of the data collected in your sample.

- **Understand and use given formulas.** This means being able to apply appropriate formulas in the right situations. It will involve finding an unknown value by substituting into the formula the values you know and then carrying out a calculation.

- **Review your methods to pick up any faults and be sure your results make sense.**

Collecting evidence

HOW TO GET YOUR EVIDENCE

What you need to do	Using formulas	Tiling a bathroom Continued from page 51
Show you can do calculations that involve amounts and sizes, scales and proportions, working with statistics, using formulas. Make sure you have a clear record of all the working out you did for each of your calculations. Work to an appropriate level of accuracy, keeping a note of what this level is and why it is appropriate. Make sure that your answers are correct by checking your calculations and correcting any mistakes.	If you were calculating the temperature in degrees Celsius you would use the formula $C = \frac{5}{9}(F - 32)$. So if your Fahrenheit reading is 76, you would set out your calculation like this: $\frac{5}{9}(76 - 32) = \frac{5}{9} \times 44$ $= 24.444$ $= 24.4 \text{ (1 dp)}$ So 76 is 24.4 °C	Having got the measurements that I will need to calculate the total area, I will work out the areas of each wall and the ceiling by multiplying the length of each wall by its height, and the length of the ceiling by the width. Before I add them together, I need to deduct the area of the window and the door from each appropriate wall. Then I can add them together to get the total area I need to tile. I will round up each wall size and the ceiling size to the nearest 10 cm to give me an appropriate margin of error and to make sure that I have slightly more than enough tiles. I will add

10 tiles to the total. This is in case I don't cut some correctly or break one or two.

I will check my answers by redoing all the calculations to ensure that I get the same answers again.

Continued on page 56

Evidence requirements in a nutshell

You need to have evidence in your portfolio showing that you can do four different types of calculation. You must show you can do calculations that are to do with:

- Amounts and sizes
- Scales and proportions
- Handling statistics
- Using formulas

Make sure that each time you do any of these calculations you have records of all the working out that you do. Include in these records how you checked your answers and how your corrected any mistakes that you found. Make sure the results of the calculations make sense. To do this you might need to check the results against your original purpose.

Hints for carrying out calculations at level 2

- Have four separate records that show your calculations to do with (a) amounts and sizes, (b) scales and proportion, (c) working with statistics, (d) using formulas.
- Maybe use them as subsections in the Calculations section of your number portfolio.
- Show your working for each calculation. It is important to keep this as a record, even if you go back over your work and find mistakes, you should keep a record of this. This is proof that you checked your own work and were able to correct it.
- Keep notes or other records showing how you worked out and what would be an appropriate level of accuracy and why you thought it was an appropriate level.

The Bottom Line

Interpreting results and presenting your findings

What you must learn to do

- **Present your findings using appropriate methods and following the appropriate conventions for labelling.** Whether you are producing pie charts, frequency tables, graphs or workshop drawings, you must show that you can correctly label your work. This is to help others read and understand your work. Remember that very often, the point of using methods like graphs or diagrams is to help others understand your work more easily. Correct labelling helps.

- **Be able to communicate your results, justify the methods you chose and be able to relate the work to your original findings or purpose.** Remember that the whole exercise is about showing you can read, interpret, calculate and present numbers to meet your different purposes or needs. So it is important to explain how your work with numbers helped you to meet your purpose. You also need to explain why you chose to do it the way you did, helping others understand the reasons for taking your decisions. This could be explaining about the equipment you used, the accuracy you worked to, the calculations you made or anything else you did. this is your chance to explain why you thought these were appropriate choices to make.

Collecting evidence

HOW TO GET YOUR EVIDENCE		
What you need to do	*Shaving foam survey*	*Tiling a bathroom* *Continued from page 55*
Look at the results from calculations you have made and identify good ways of presenting this information. Present the information clearly. Explain why you think the ways you have chosen to present your results are effective and the most appropriate. When you are producing evidence for this section, make sure you will have at least one graph, one chart and one diagram in your portfolio.	I have collected the results of a survey to see how effective a supermarket's promotional display of shaving foam is. I wanted to see how many people bought the display brand on promotion and how many bought alternative brands not on promotion. To do this I observed the shoppers for one hour by standing near the shaving foam products. I used the tally method to record my results.	Having got the area of the room to be tiled, I can show the cost of using differently priced tiles in a bar chart. The x-axis will have the different types of tiles and the y-axis will show the prices. Before I can draw the bar chart I need to work out how much the tiles will cost. This will mean working out how many of each of the tiles will be needed to cover the area of the bathroom. I will work out how much that number of that particular tile will

Describe how your results help you meet the purpose of your task.

There were 32 shoppers who bought shaving foam, 18 of these people chose the brand on promotion.

I think the most appropriate way to present this data visually is to use a pie chart. Turning my results into a pie chart means dividing 18 by 33 then multiplying the answer by 360. The answer is 196 to the nearest whole number. I will need to draw a sector of angle 196°.

When I talk about the results, I will describe them as a percentage (%). This will mean dividing 18 by 33 then multiplying by 100. The answer is 55% (rounded to the nearest whole number). I could even present the results as a ratio. This means showing the ratio of shoppers who bought the promotional shaving foam to those who bought another brand.

I could use all the working out as evidence for the Calculations section of my portfolio.

cost. Then I can draw the bar chart.

This will give me a good visual image showing the variation in the cost of using different tiles.

Evidence requirements in a nutshell

You need to show that you can select good ways to present the number information you have collected or created using your calculations. It is important to keep records explaining the reasons for the choices you are making when you select different ways to present information. This helps the person marking your work to understand your thinking.

Somewhere in this part of your portfolio you will have to show you can present information using a graph, a chart and a diagram that you have created. You will also need to include in your work a note explaining how the results of your calculations meet your purpose.

Hints for interpreting results and presenting your findings at level 2

- Make sure each of your charts and diagrams has clear labels and a title that explains what it shows.
- Make sure you have used the correct units of measurement for what you have measured.
- Check that you have used appropriate scales and axes.
- Remember to give evidence that you can present your information using at least one graph, one chart and one diagram.

Other forms of assessment and evidence

External assessment at levels 1 and 2

You will need to take an external assessment as well as produce a portfolio of number evidence. The external assessment is designed to show that you can work with numbers at the correct level under a different set of circumstances. Normally, for your portfolio work, you will try to use the other courses that you are doing as a way of helping generate your number evidence. This time, in the external assessment, you will not know what the questions are.

What will the external assessment ask questions about?

The external assessment can only ask you questions on the number key skill. Therefore, everything that is asked has to be based on what is in the key skill specification. You cannot be asked something that is not based on the key skill specification at the level you are taking. The people who write the tests know this and have been told to make sure they stick to the number work in the key skill.

All this means that you really know what type of questions will be asked in the external assessment. You may not know exactly what each question will be about, but you will know what level they will be set at and you will know the type of number work that will be involved.

Normally, external assessments will be set by your key skills awarding body and may involve a series of tasks about numbers that you must do within a certain time period. The fact that the questions are set and marked or the marking is checked by someone not in the school or college is what makes them 'external'. These types of assessment might be called external assignments, controlled assignments or just tests. Check with your teacher to find out more about how your Application of Number key skill will be externally assessed.

Even if you are allowed to use your calculator, remember that it will also be important to write down all your working clearly.

What is the point of an external assessment?

The idea of an external assessment is that someone else sets you a series of related number tasks. That way you can show that you can carry out different number work to complete tasks set by other people. Your portfolio shows that you can carry out number work based on your own number tasks.

It is also attempting to show that you can do larger, related tasks than can be asked in a test but still do them under controlled conditions (a time limit and with someone else setting the tasks). Here is how to look at it:

- The portfolio shows that you can set your own number tasks, you can carry them out with and without a calculator, and you can meet your own deadlines and time limits.
- The external assessments show that you can do number work in a restricted amount of time. You will know what the questions are likely to involve but you will not know exactly what they are about.
- The external assessments also show that you can carry out larger number tasks set by other people, and do them within the set time limits.

When you meet these requirements, you will get your key skill in Application of Number, and you will have proved that you can do the number work under a range of different conditions and in different contexts.

What? No calculator!

The external assessment is also checking to see that you are not completely dependent on a calculator to work with numbers. What you should be doing during the course of your key skills portfolio work is practising doing appropriate calculations without a calculator and then using a calculator to check your work. You have plenty of time to develop your mental powers, if you start practising at the beginning of the course.

Remember that you will be given paper to work things out and you must start getting into the habit of writing down your working clearly so that others can follow it. This is vital for your portfolio work and your test. So get into this habit immediately.

There may well be an external assessment that allows you to use a calculator and one that does not. Check with your teacher how the key skill is to be externally assessed and what the rules about calculators will be so you can prepare appropriately.

Part 3: Opportunities

This part highlights opportunities for generating number evidence in the qualifications you are taking. It will show you:

- How your qualifications can be used to generate number evidence.
- Where the best opportunities for this evidence arise in the qualifications.

This part is divided into three sections:

- **Evidence from GCSE courses**: You will find this section useful whichever awarding body you are with.
- **Evidence from GNVQ courses**: This section will be useful at both foundation and intermediate level, regardless of whether you are working towards a full award or a Part One award.
- **Evidence from everyday sources**: This section will show you how you already use numbers as part of your everyday life.

The examples provided should be seen as starting points for generating evidence. You will see that some qualifications provide more opportunities than others. However, all contain some opportunities and will at least get you started. Make sure that you take time to read not just your subjects but also subjects that are related to the ones you are taking. This will help you gain a fuller understanding of how and where number evidence can be produced. For example, if you are doing a Business GNVQ then also look at the Business Studies GCSE and the Retail and Distributive Services GNVQ. You may also want to check out the Leisure and Tourism GNVQ.

Vocational awards
The GNVQ Advanced awards are now called Vocational A-levels. From September 2001 GNVQ Foundation and Intermediate awards are likely to be known as Vocational GCSEs.

Evidence from GCSE courses

Art GCSE

About the syllabus

The Art award aims to help you develop your creative, imaginative and practical skills as you work in art, craft and design. You will also have the opportunity to explore historical and contemporary sources and make practical and critical judgements and responses.

See also: **Art and Design GNVQ**, page 81

Topic area
Images and artefacts

Planning and interpreting information

The quality of your work in art, craft and design will be judged by the images and artefacts that you produce. Images and artefacts are the result of careful and detailed observations that are accurately and thoughtfully recorded. You will produce these using a variety of approaches. One way of working is interpreting what you see, using your existing numerical skills in a very practical way.

Everything you look at provides information in some form or another:

- An accurate representational drawing relies on your ability to use scale and proportion appropriately as well as translate 3D measurements into 2D.
- The production of an artefact from an original drawing requires you to be able to read and understand the original sketches as well as to estimate the amount of materials required.
- Many aspects of art, craft and design rely upon your ability to interpret visual information from a range of sources. This requires you to be competent and confident in basic numeracy. You are likely to use these skills almost without thinking, but you must record the occasions on which you use them so that they can provide evidence for your key skill.

Calculating

Most of the calculations you will do while drawing will be mental calculations as you scale up or scale down when placing and producing an image on canvas or paper. However, the creating of artefacts will normally require you to work with materials and technology. Here calculations have a role to play as you work out the amount of materials needed, the ratios of chemicals to be mixed, the drying or setting times necessary, or simply use formulas for areas and volumes when building or casting. Throughout your work you will be using a range of methods to check that your practice will be effective and produce the results you are seeking.

Interpreting results and presenting findings

A central requirement of your course is that you 'realise your intentions'. This will usually be done when you present your work. You can do so in a display or within your portfolio. You will need to think carefully about the best way to do this. You may need to keep charts, sketches, models or photographs to record how the work has progressed. Annotated sketches that show the development of your thinking about size, colour, shape or structure should be considered as working diagrams in this context. All artists evaluate their work. This involves saying what went well, what did not, and what you have learned for future projects.

Topic area 2
Personal project

Planning and interpreting information

All Art awards will expect you to undertake a personal project as part of the course. The programme expects you to develop skills for working across all aspects of art, craft and design and you will have the opportunity to produce work from direct experience, observation or imagination using any medium, material or technology available. This opportunity can be a rich source for key skills evidence. Choose a subject that allows you to look at many different sources as a starting point. They need not all be visual; many artists are stimulated by the relationship of numbers, or the juxtaposition of ideas and attitudes. You may even wish to collect other people's ideas and views and use them as a source or starting point. Make sure you keep careful records of the sources of your ideas, through sketches and notes.

Calculating

The extent to which calculations are involved will depend upon the focus of your project. Always make sure that you clearly identify where you have worked out amounts or sizes or scales and proportions as well as showing how they have contributed to your development.

Interpreting results and presenting findings

You are required to make 'critical judgements' about your work in art, craft and design, using a specialist vocabulary. Make sure that your presentation is appropriate to your original intentions, describe the contribution that numeracy has made to your work and, where possible, use annotated drawings and records that chart the progress of the work.

Further opportunities for evidence

Other people's art, craft and design

You are expected to show an appreciation and understanding of the work of other artists, craftspeople and designers and make connections between it and your own work. These investigations will lead you to look at a range of different sources: primary sources such as visits to museums and galleries; and secondary sources such as books and the internet. You should look carefully at how other creative individuals have used number as a tool when designing and making, and as a creative influence when making aesthetic decisions.

Galleries and museums

You will have the opportunity to see examples of art, craft and design at a range of locations which will be commercially, privately or state run. They all depend on numbers for their existence. This dependency ranges from the number of pieces sold and the prices charged to the number of visitors to the exhibitions and the comments they make. An analysis of how exhibitions are organised and how galleries and museums are run, provides an opportunity for you to see another side of the creative industry and how important number is to its survival.

What you must know
Part 1: The Learning Curve will help you with the knowledge you need.

What you must do
Part 2: The Bottom Line will help you with the evidence you need.

Business Studies GCSE

About the syllabus

The Business Studies award aims to help you develop your ability to apply your numerical knowledge, techniques and understanding of how businesses work in a wide range of contexts. You will be required to evaluate the strengths and limitations of ideas and distinguish between facts and opinions using a range of data to inform your judgement.

Topic area 1
The aims and objectives of business

Planning and interpreting information

See also: **Business GNVQ**, page 85

You will be expected to understand how an organisation works within a range of economic, political and social contexts. You will need to understand how organisations work, including their structure, the nature of their business, their aims and objectives and the criteria for judging success. To do this you will need to learn how to select, organise and interpret information from a range of sources. This could be statistical data from company reports, business manuals or consumer reports and tables on particular businesses.

You must ensure that all the information you collect is accurate and reliable and that it is recorded in an appropriate form. By doing this you will provide yourself with accessible data for use in evaluating effective business operations and acceptable evidence for your application of number.

Calculating

To be effective a business must show that it can create wealth, secure a reasonable market share and show a profit. Your work on particular businesses will require you to examine how a business survives in a competitive world. You will be expected to work with large numbers, percentages and different sets of data as you use the information you have collected, to analyse performance.

Interpreting results and presenting findings

Your analysis of businesses, their functions and their success or failure should be based on your interpretation of your calculations and your results. You must present your findings using the normal business conventions such as flow charts, tables of statistical data and graphs of projected growth in sales or income. You must make sure that the methods you select to present your information are clear. Always check that your presentation and results relate to the original purpose of the activity. A careful, well reasoned and recorded evaluation will provide evidence for your Application of Number portfolio.

Topic area 2
The management of finance

Planning and interpreting information

An effective business relies upon the availability of finance. You will be expected to show how businesses secure, use and manage money. This will include:

- The identification of initial capital
- The function of balance sheets
- Using forecasting to maintain cash flow

You will need to select, organise and interpret a range of different types of data and information from company reports as well as government bulletins and consumer reports. This is likely to involve you in working with and understanding information presented in a range of formats, written and graphical. Always make sure that your records are carefully organised, authentic and valid for your purposes.

Calculating

You will be expected to be able to read simple balance sheets and use your numerical skills to calculate profit and, where necessary, loss. You may have the opportunity to work with different sets of data to show percentage increases or to project future performance. Always make sure that you check your calculations before making judgements or interpreting your results.

Interpreting results and presenting findings

Your analysis of the sources, uses and management of finance in a par-

ticular business should produce a wealth of numerical information. You will need to select and present this information carefully, using tables, charts and graphs where appropriate, to ensure that you explain your findings clearly and unambiguously.

Further opportunities for evidence

Production and marketing

All businesses have a product and all products must have a market if the business is to survive. An analysis of how individual businesses work out the relationship between development and production costs and selling price will provide you with a wealth of numerical information for collection, interpretation, calculation and explanation.

Equally, how a business identifies or creates a market then promotes the product is a topic that is rich in key skills opportunities. You will have the opportunity to explore market research and promotional techniques as well as how price can be manipulated to increase sales and secure market share.

What you must know
Part 1: The Learning Curve will help you with the knowledge you need.

What you must do
Part 2: The Bottom Line will help you with the evidence you need.

Design and Technology GCSE

About the syllabus

The Design and Technology award aims to help you develop your knowledge and understanding of designing so that you can work with appropriate and suitable design specifications. You will be expected to develop your making skills by applying knowledge and understanding of relevant processes, materials and techniques and using materials, tools and equipment.

See also: **Engineering GNVQ**, page 89 and **Manufacturing GNVQ**, page 107

Topic area 1
Working with a design specification

Planning and interpreting information

A design specification can be presented orally, supported by diagrams or drawings or in the form of a written text supported by other relevant data. The process by which you interpret this specification, analyse the requirements, calculate the materials, identify the technology or equipment necessary and prepare for making, provides sufficient evidence for all aspects of the Application of Number key skill.

The sources of information will be the design specification itself and any specialist information or manuals you need to consult in terms of media, materials or equipment. Make sure that you read and record these sources carefully.

Calculating

The outcome of a design specification is a product or artefact. The product or artefact will need to be made out of media and materials which will need to be identified (amounts and sizes), having been scaled up from the original diagrams or drawings (scales and proportions) and costed (using formulas). The process of identifying media and materials and preparing for the making process is likely to generate extensive evidence of your ability to apply your numerical skills effectively.

Interpreting results and presenting findings

The process of ordering or securing access to the appropriate media, materials and technology can be used as a presentational opportunity. You can present your calculations and findings in an appropriate form using tables, charts and annotated diagrams or drawings. This stage may be used to persuade the provider of the original design specification of the strength of your design solution and the need for better quality materials or a greater budget for realisation.

Topic area 2
Making skills

Planning and interpreting information

Before you begin to make, you must ensure that you have a full understanding of the original specification and that you have assembled all the media, materials and equipment necessary for you to work efficiently. You will need to read the measurements given in diagrams and drawings and transfer them accurately to materials when preparing for cutting, forming or joining. You may also need to read tables and charts when preparing to use specialist equipment, especially where time and temperature are involved. All aspects of your interpretation may result in a detailed production plan.

Calculating

Calculating *during*, rather than *when preparing for*, making will usually concern amount and sizes, particularly when looking at multiple production or repeat patterns and forms. It is especially important that these calculations are checked carefully before actually cutting, forming or joining is done, to ensure that errors do not result in wastage or shortage of materials.

Interpreting results and presenting findings

The products or artefacts you make will provide the focus of your presentation. This will determine the success of your interpretation of the original design specification and your resulting calculations. Make sure that you support your final outcome with working drawings, annotated diagrams and a production schedule. The final product specification may also be set out in a table.

The extent to which your work in design and technology provides evidence for the substantial activity that includes straightforward tasks for carrying out calculations will depend upon how accurately, carefully and logically you have recorded the integrated activities that are part of the making process and design realisation.

Further opportunities for evidence

Class work activities

Your learning opportunities will show you have to measure and decide on the media and materials you need. This will involve separate tasks in which you will calculate:

- Amounts and sizes of sheet materials.
- Scales and proportion as you use original scale drawings to decide on real amounts of materials.
- Using formulas to find areas of sheet materials and volumes of casting materials during pre-production exercises.

Course work assignments

Your programme of study will require you to undertake a project in which you will be expected to combine your design skills with your making skills. This will provide you with a further opportunity to demonstrate effective application of your number skills as you seek, select, use and interpret design ideas to promote outcomes that match agreed criteria.

What you must know
Part 1: The Learning Curve will help you with the knowledge you need.

What you must do
Part 2: The Bottom Line will help you with the evidence you need.

Geography GCSE

About the syllabus

The Geography award aims to help you to develop your knowledge and understanding of places, environments and patterns on local and global scales. You are required to use your developing knowledge and understanding to show an appreciation of the environment and human interaction with it. You will do this by developing and applying a range of skills, many of which are identical to the skills you will use in the application of number. They include:

- Identification and collection of evidence using primary sources (fieldwork) and secondary sources (maps and statistics)
- Recording your findings and results (maps, graphs and diagrams)
- Evaluating, analysing evidence and presenting it in numerical, graphical and written forms.

Topic area 1
Fieldwork

A fieldwork exercise is a substantial activity and should include aspects of the three separate tasks for which you have to provide evidence to achieve application of number at level 2. If you work on only some of these tasks, or if you have a lot of help, you will produce evidence for level 1 only.

Planning and interpreting information

A fieldwork exercise will provide you with two different sources of information:

- **The secondary source**: maps, surveys or written descriptions of the site produced by others. You will usually use this source first in order to plan and prepare adequately for the exercise.
- **The primary source**: the site itself, where you can make first-hand observations and measurements of physical features and record them on sketches, maps or diagrams. Always make sure that you use appropriate measuring instruments then take and record measurements accurately using appropriate units.

Calculating

Most of this work will usually be done away from the site, so it is important that you collect and record numerical information accurately and fully. It is often helpful to make some estimations or approximations of what you think your calculations should produce while you are on site, to make sure that your results are in line with reality and make sense. Here are the three types of evidence you are likely to produce:

- **Maps and diagrams** will require you to work with scales and proportion.
- **Surveys and observations** will require you to compare sets of data and handle statistics.
- **Environmental science tasks** will require you to understand and use formulas.

Interpreting results and presenting findings

Your field study will provide you with a wealth of different evidence that will need to be presented in a range of different ways. Look carefully at what you have and what you want to explain and show. Choose different ways to present your information. A balance between written words, diagrams and graphs, tables and charts will help you to present different information appropriately.

Topic area 2
Economic matters

Planning and interpreting information

Economic geography will usually be taught using secondary sources such as:

- Population figures and distributions – local, regional and national
- Trade figures, including import/export statistics and exchange rates
- Reports and research papers from national governments and the European Union

These sources will provide you with an opportunity to obtain information that is relevant to your enquiry.

Calculating

You will be expected to extract, group and compare data using frequency

tables and diagrams. You may be expected to express ratios and proportions using decimals, fractions or percentages. This is particularly important when describing growth or decay in areas such as the economy or employment figures.

Interpreting results and presenting findings

Statistical work provides an ideal opportunity for you to use a range of methods to present your findings. Make sure that:

- Graphical material uses the proper conventions such as labels and scales.
- Explanations are given in the context of your original purpose.
- Conclusions are supported by the evidence you present.
- Inconsistencies or errors are explained by you and not found by others.

What you must know
Part 1: The Learning Curve will help you with the knowledge you need.

What you must do
Part 2: The Bottom Line will help you with the evidence you need.

History GCSE

About the syllabus

The History award aims to help you develop your understanding of how the past has been represented and interpreted and how you can use this awareness to examine historical sources critically. You are required to use your developing knowledge and understanding of the past alongside skills of investigation, analysis, interpretation and evaluation, to draw conclusions about the periods, societies or situations studied.

You may think that the key skills of Application of Number are relevant to the study of history but you would be wrong. Your history course is unlikely to give you the opportunity to generate all of the evidence for the key skill portfolio. However, it should provide you with plenty of opportunities to develop and use your number skills when you:

- Read, understand and use numbers in different ways for dates and times.
- Read, understand and use graphical sources such as diagrams and maps.
- Read, understand and use statistical sources such as mortality rates during the Plague or levels of unemployment during the Great Depression.
- Collect first-hand information during historical visits, such as surveying battlefield sites.

Topic area 1
Chronological order

Planning and interpreting information

Although you can study history from other perspectives besides time (i.e. when things happened), to have a real understanding of the past you must be able to place events in their chronological context. Numbers are used as a shorthand way of doing this because they represent dates and times. This is such a simple idea, and you will probably be so used to it, that you will have forgotten how important it is.

Numbers are used in history to show the passage of time. In application of number this means read and understand numbers used in different ways. For example, do you really understand the meaning of BC and AD? They actually signify a number line between negative and positive numbers. Date lines are important in history when you begin to put events in the correct sequence or chronological order, or see how others have done this.

Your knowledge and understanding will depend upon your grasp of chronological order. The sources of information you read will give you dates of events and times of actions. In history, order and sequence are critical. You must be able to look at written sources and identify how events unfold. In this way you can begin to understand cause and effect. Having a grasp of who did what and when will help you understand how things happened. A good example of the importance of sequence in making sense of historical facts is the events leading up to the First World War and Bismarck's role in it.

Calculating

The time between events is as important as the dates of the events themselves. Much of the reason for this is to do with technological developments. In the 1990s, if one country launched a nuclear attack on another, the country being attacked would know in seconds and could respond in a suitable timescale; but back in the 1790s information travelled so much slower and response rates were equally slow. You need to understand these sorts of thing when working out how events are linked.

In this area the calculations you will be required to perform will be simple, straightforward sums to do with amounts and sizes that will help you to find out how long something took and how far apart events were. This will help you to find out if they could be linked.

Interpreting results and presenting findings

Your analysis of chronology and sequence of events will help you present an explanation of how an event took place. You might examine the specific events leading up to:

- The Spanish Armada
- Oliver Cromwell and the Commonwealth
- The American War of Independence
- The Second World War

You will be used to presenting your work in written form but you can provide numerical data in history using a table or a chart to identify the key dates and events and show how they are linked. You may also want to draw a diagram or date line that shows the sequence of dates and times.

The way in which you present your historical information and the use you make of graphical, numerical and written material will provide you

with valid evidence to meet both the *interpreting* and the *interpreting and presenting* aspects of the key skill.

Topic area 2
Historical sources

Planning and interpreting information
You will be expected to understand historical events by reading how they were reported at the time. Recent history is easier to access because we have newspapers and other primary sources to draw on. This is not so easy when we go further back in history, because the style of the language in which events are recorded, the spelling and even particular words can be very different. Primary sources have a very important role in your understanding of history and this understanding will depend in part on your ability to find and extract information recorded numerically. This could be in the form of:

- **Maps, charts and diagrams of battles or journeys**. The Spanish Armada is often most clearly understood through the study of a map that shows the Armada's journey from Spain to England, the fireship attack at Calais, followed by the eventual dispersal of the fleet in the North Sea and then Ireland.
- **Tables and lists**. Merchants' ledgers are useful when investigating the slave trade and the monetary value placed on human life; simple household records of the nineteenth century reveal how income and expenditure were carefully monitored and balanced.
- **A survey of an historical site**. You are likely at some time to have the opportunity, through school or college or on your own, to carry out some personal research of an event, person or issue. A visit to an historical site such as Corbridge in Durham would give you the opportunity to analyse how the Romans lived by examining plans and scale drawings of the site, and how their military might was organised. Depending on your focus, you could make further observations to do with how this site is used as a source by others.

Calculating

What you must know
Part 1: The Learning Curve will help you with the knowledge you need.

Opportunities for calculations will depend upon the topic you are studying, such as a topic involving sets of data taken from statistical records. Surveys of historical sites and the production of accurate maps or diagrams could provide you with opportunities to work with scales and ratios.

Interpreting results and presenting findings
The extent to which you can provide Application of Number evidence will depend upon how you present your findings. You should take every opportunity to show what you have discovered in ways not usually expected by your teachers. The charts, diagrams and graphs required by Application of Number could help you to make your work more original and effective.

What you must do
Part 2: The Bottom Line will help you with the evidence you need.

Home Economics GCSE

CHILD DEVELOPMENT • CONSUMER STUDIES • TEXTILES • FOOD AND NUTRITION

About the syllabus

The Home Economics awards aim to help you develop the knowledge and skills required to organise and manage resources effectively and safely. You will have the opportunity to increase your awareness of the impact of social, cultural and economic factors as well as your awareness of technological developments on individuals and groups. You will be expected to apply this knowledge and understanding in order to respond appropriately and effectively to investigations and tasks within the subject.

Topic area 1
Investigating existing sources

An essential skill for home economics will be your ability to plan and carry out investigations and tasks that are set by your programme of study. The skills you will use will be the same for all different aspects of the subject and you will be expected to gather, record, collate, interpret and evaluate evidence. These skills match the different aspects of Application of Number: interpreting information, calculating and presenting findings.

Planning and interpreting information

You will be expected to identify sources of information and evidence and select relevant information and data from these sources. The exact sources and the way the information is presented will depend upon the investigation or task but it is likely that you will need to read and understand straightforward tables, charts and diagrams. Here are some examples:

- **Child development:** when you read tables of dietary values or graphs representing a baby's physical development.
- **Consumer studies:** when you analyse statistical data on consumer needs.
- **Food and nutrition:** when you read tables of food additives or charts and diagrams from health guides.
- **Textiles:** when you read tables and charts which classify fibres.

You will be expected to present any relevant data in a form which is clear and logical and, if necessary, available for calculation or manipulation.

Calculating

Collecting data from a variety of sources will require you to understand and present numbers in the same form. Numerical information is often presented in decimals, fractions, percentages and ratios. You will be

expected to accurately convert all information to the same form so that you can compare and evaluate this data.

You may also need to convert from one set of measurements to another. For instance, any historical records may use imperial measurements such as inches, pounds and ounces or pints and gallons. You will need to convert them to metric measurements to ensure that your records and results are meaningful to others.

All aspects of this subject rely on statistics, either in written form or graphical form. You will be required to group data to make sure that your results are clear to others. Here are some opportunities:

- **Child development:** when you are comparing growth and development rates in a group of children.
- **Consumer studies:** when you are comparing choices of goods or services used by different age groups or different socio-economic backgrounds based on income.
- **Food and nutrition:** when comparing cooking or preparation times for different foods, using different types of equipment such as electric, gas or microwave ovens.
- **Textiles:** when you are comparing costs of production of different textile items and the reasons for these costs.

At all stages, check that your results make sense and are accurate, particularly when converting from one measurement or number system to another.

Interpreting results and presenting findings

Your analysis and investigations will provide you with results that you will have to interpret, evaluate and present to others. You will be expected to use methods that help you explain clearly and logically what you have found out.

If your findings are to provide evidence for your Application of Number key skill, you will have to use charts, diagrams and graphs to explain how these findings are connected to the original task. You can use the original sources to help you decide what will be the most effective methods to use.

Topic area 2
Investigating using own sources

Planning and interpreting information

You will be expected to use your own observations to collect and record information and data. This will involve you in planning the source of your information, deciding what equipment to use and what measurements are most appropriate to accurately record your observations. The extent to which this activity provides valid application of number evidence will depend upon how you record your observations and prepare the data for calculating.

Calculating

You will need to show your methods and calculations clearly and make sure that you work to an appropriate level of accuracy. This is likely to require you to round your findings up or down.

Observation data can be grouped and compared using mean, median and mode. This will provide you with the opportunity to show your ability to handle statistics and show how your results can support reasoned and relevant conclusions.

Interpreting results and presenting information

You will need to review your results, present your information clearly and draw conclusions that meet the purpose of your original activity, investigation or task. Always use graphical material to support your findings and make sure that you follow accepted conventions for labelling.

Further opportunities for evidence

Class work activities

Your learning opportunities will provide you with a range of individual tasks that can generate evidence for the individual aspects of the Application of Number key skill. The extent to which this evidence can be used in your portfolio will depend upon the degree of independence you show and the accuracy and relevance of this work.

Course work activities

Your programme of study requires you to undertake a project in which you will be expected to recall and apply your knowledge and understanding of home economics issues. This will provide you with a further opportunity to carry out a substantial activity that includes seeking, selecting, using and interpreting numerical data in the context of your project.

What you must know
Part 1: The Learning Curve will help you with the knowledge you need.

What you must do
Part 2: The Bottom Line will help you with the evidence you need.

Mathematics GCSE

About the syllabus

The Mathematics award aims to help you develop the ability to use and apply mathematics in solving everyday problems, in thinking clearly and logically and in effective communication. To do this you will be expected to have a good understanding of number and algebra; shape, space and measures; and data handling.

Topic area 1
Using and applying mathematics

Planning and interpreting information

You will be expected to deal with real problems, simulations or tasks set in a range of contexts. You will need to make sure that you

understand the purpose of the activity and then identify and obtain relevant information from different sources. You may need to use primary sources where you record your own measurements or observations, or secondary sources where you interpret information from written or graphical material. Whatever sources you use, make sure that you read and record carefully and that you understand the numbers or measurements you are working with. You will also need to think ahead to the calculations you expect to do and use units of measurement in a form that allows you to manipulate numbers easily (calculate).

Calculating

The calculations you carry out will depend upon the problems, situations or tasks you are working on and the contexts in which they are set. You must make sure that you carefully and clearly show all your working out and, where possible, provide evidence that you have checked your results and corrected any errors.

Many real-world contexts will require you to work with a range of measurements. Sometimes this involves conversions within a system, e.g. metres to centimetres; other times between measurement systems, e.g. Celsius to Fahrenheit. Always show how this has been done, recording any rounding up or down and any relevant formulas.

Interpreting results and presenting findings

You may overlook this aspect of mathematics if you believe that once you have an answer this is enough. Both mathematics and application of number expect you to understand what you have done and why you have done it and to explain how your findings meet the purpose of the original activity. Demonstrating these aspects will require you to use a range of different methods – oral, written and graphical – to represent your findings. Here are some possible options:

- A flow diagram can show the stages of a calculation.
- A table can show how you compared different measurements.
- An annotated scale drawing or diagram can show dimensions or distances.
- A graph can record observations and make projections.

Topic area 2
Handling data

Planning and interpreting information

You will be expected to read and understand graphs, tables, charts and diagrams from a range of different sources. They may be given to you by others or identified by you. You may also be expected to generate your own data from questionnaires or direct observation.

All data should be carefully recorded and, where necessary, presented in appropriate groups according to size or measures. When collecting and recording data, make sure that you are aware of how you will manipulate it at the next stage of development.

Calculating

You will be expected to understand, calculate and use mean, median and mode to compare sets of data. This will provide you with the opportunity to use formulas such as $\frac{1}{2}(n+1)$ for median. You may also show how distribution and range of data contribute to your line of enquiry by selection of appropriate statistics.

Activities involving probability will provide you with an opportunity to work with fractions, decimals and percentages and show how frequency and probability can be represented in a range of equivalent forms.

Interpreting results and presenting findings

You will be expected to use the full range of graphical methods including line graphs, pie charts, frequency diagrams and histograms to interpret your results and present your findings. You will be required to understand and show how different averages can be used to provide different interpretations of statistical evidence and how sampling and different sample sizes can affect the reliability of conclusions made.

Work involving probability will provide you with the opportunity to use tree diagrams to represent the full range of projected outcomes including multi-stage activities and at level 2 an understanding of conditional probability.

Further opportunities for evidence

Class work activities

Your learning opportunities will provide you with a range of individual tasks which will expect you to interpret information, calculate using number, algebra, space, shapes and measurements as well as present and explain your findings and results. The extent to which these individual tasks provide you with valid Application of Number evidence will depend upon how your number skills are selected and applied. The most appropriate evidence will come from using your skills in combination with information and data drawn from courses, programmes or activities outside mathematics lessons themselves.

Course work activities

Depending on your programme of study, you may have the opportunity to work on a personal project that contributes to your Mathematics GCSE. If chosen carefully, this project can also provide evidence for Application of Number at level 2 because it should be a substantial activity that includes discrete tasks of interpreting information, calculating and interpreting results, and presenting findings. Make sure that you record and explain your decisions carefully as well as how your results relate to the original purpose of the project.

What you must know
Part 1: The Learning Curve will help you with the knowledge you need.

What you must do
Part 2: The Bottom Line will help you with the evidence you need.

Science GCSE
BIOLOGY • CHEMISTRY • PHYSICS

About the syllabus
The Science awards aim to help you develop scientific knowledge and understanding and how to apply them to experiments and investigations. You will have the opportunity to develop an understanding of the power of scientific ideas and the limitations of scientific claims. You will be expected to appreciate the technological and environmental applications of science within economic, ethical and social contexts and constraints.

See also: **Science GNVQ**, page 118

Topic area 1
Experimenting and investigating

Planning and interpreting information
An essential scientific skill is your ability to plan procedures, make accurate measurements and observations then select and record relevant information and data. The experiments and investigations you do during your science courses will provide you with the opportunity to collect information from primary sources by measuring and observing. You will also be expected to use apparatus and equipment accurately and safely, and read scales and measurements to appropriate levels of accuracy. You will be expected to record measurements or observations using tables, charts or diagrams to show your approach to the experiment or investigation.

Calculating
When analysing your initial information, data and findings, you will be required to set out any calculations clearly and systematically. You should always work to agreed levels of accuracy by rounding up or down and you should always use established conventions, including abbreviations and chemical symbols.

The actual mathematical calculations you will use will depend upon the focus of your calculations. Opportunities are likely for you to:

- Group and compare sets of data in experiments to do with life processes and living things.
- Use formulas for balanced equations in investigations of physical processes.
- Work with amounts and sizes, scales and proportions when experimenting or investigating materials and their properties.

Any calculations must be carefully checked and, if necessary, repeated or corrected to ensure the results make sense.

Interpreting results and presenting findings
Your experiments and investigations will produce outcomes or results which will need evaluating, explaining and, if necessary, used as the basis

for predictions. You will be expected to choose the most effective ways to present your findings and predictions and support your arguments.

Both your science and key skills work require you to use a range of graphical methods, graphs, charts and diagrams to explain your results and show how your findings meet the original purpose of your experiment or investigation. Your work in this area is ideally suited to meeting the Application of Number requirement at level 2 for you to carry out a substantial activity that includes evidence of interpretation, calculation and presentation.

Topic area 2
Observations, ideas and arguments

Planning and interpreting information

Your programme of study will provide you with the opportunity to explore and communicate the scientific observations, ideas and arguments of others in biology, chemistry and physics. To do this effectively, you will need to obtain information from secondary sources by reading and understanding written and graphical material. You will be expected to read and understand numbers of different sizes including negative numbers. The precise use of these numbers will depend upon the context and nature of the observations, ideas and arguments explored. You may expect to read and understand:

- Tables of values when working on materials and their values.
- Diagrams of experimental procedures when working on physical processes.
- Charts and graphs when working on life processes and living things.

You will be expected to select the information and data and record in it forms that are clear and relevant to the tasks in hand.

Calculating

You will be expected to apply and combine your scientific and mathematical knowledge, skills and understanding to test out the validity of other people's observations, ideas and arguments. The range of scientific information and data you work with will determine the exact nature of the mathematical routines and calculations you will do. Make sure that you show your working methods at all times and check for accuracy at key points during the process.

Interpreting and presenting findings

You must present your conclusions clearly, logically and systematically, using both scientific knowledge and technical vocabulary to explain how these conclusions relate to your original purpose. An effective presentation will draw together the full range of data and information from a variety of sources; it will define your findings using scientific and mathematical conventions; and it will describe outcomes using scientific and technical vocabulary with precision.

What you must know

Part 1: The Learning Curve will help you with the knowledge you need.

What you must do

Part 2: The Bottom Line will help you with the evidence you need.

Further opportunities for evidence

Class work activities

Your learning opportunities will provide you with a range of individual tasks that will expect you to read and understand a range of graphical material, use your mathematical knowledge and skills and present results. These opportunities may be as discrete tasks or combined under one activity. The extent to which class work can provide valid evidence will depend upon the accuracy and relevance of your results and the degree of independence you show in completing the tasks. You should expect to practice these skills whenever possible, even if they do not produce evidence for assessment.

Evidence from GNVQ courses

Art and Design GNVQ

PART ONE • FOUNDATION • INTERMEDIATE

About the specifications

The Art and Design awards include the study of topics like working with materials; developing, exploring and recording; techniques and technology; and designing and making. Remember that these topics will help you generate Application of Number evidence. Your use of number skills may also help you improve your srt and fesign grades.

Topic area 1
Developing, exploring and recording by combining practical skills and ideas

See also: **Art GCSE**, page 62

Planning and interpreting information

Observing the world around you and using it as a basis for developing your ideas is an important part of art and design. You will need to be able to look and carefully record using the skills of mark-making and object-making. These activities will require you to apply your numerical skills in a very practical way. Here are some common tasks that may involve the use of quantities and units:

- **Time:** minutes (min) and seconds (s) when using photography.
- **Length:** metres (m), centimetres (cm) and millimetres (mm) when drawing, constructing or joining.
- **Volume:** cubic metres (m^3), cubic centimetres (cm^3) when modelling or forming.
- **Mass:** kilograms (kg) and grams (g) when casting or throwing.
- **Temperature:** degrees Celsius (°C) when baking or firing.

Besides knowing and understanding when to use these measurements and units, you will be able to work out the exact quantities by reading tables, charts, diagrams or graphs from instruction booklets, leaflets or manuals.

Remember that you should keep evidence to show you were able to interpret information to help you develop, explore and record using visual language.

Calculating

In art, craft and design work it is common to use ratios and proportions to help you mix different materials. For example, when casting using plaster of Paris you mix two parts of plaster to one part of water. Other examples of ratios include mixing chemicals for different resins or glues or for developing and printing in photography.

Interpreting results and presenting information

Presenting your work is a natural part of art, craft and design. Make sure any development is supported by notes or records that show how you achieved your results. They should include your technical experience as well as your creative experience. You may wish to include examples of the charts, graphs or diagrams that have helped you develop and explore your use of visual language. When you have chosen to ignore technical instructions in order to explore new ideas, you should be able to describe the effects or outcomes and explain how they have developed your understanding and capability in the skill.

Topic area 2
Using materials, techniques and technology

Planning and interpreting information

Carrying out well-organised investigations of combinations of 2D media, 3D materials and making techniques are important aspects of creative work in art, craft and design. You will need to become familiar with dry media, wet media, technological media, resistant and non-resistant materials. Each of these media and materials is described and its correct use explained by technical instruction leaflets or guidance manuals. You will need to show that you have read, understood and can use the information you have learned. Here are some common activities associated with finding out about media and materials:

- Reading leaflets on qualities of the media and materials.
- Understanding and using equipment for specialist processes accurately, including drying prints, preparing clay and firing a kiln.
- Identifying the calculations you need to make to get the results you want when using technological media.

Calculating

You will have the opportunity to use calculations to achieve the results you want when working with media and materials. For example, when mixing media or using certain materials, equipment and techniques, you will need to carry out calculations to do with amounts and sizes and use scales and proportions. Any work with photography or ceramics will involve calculations and estimations to do with time and temperature and may involve using simple formulas.

Interpreting results and presenting findings

You are required to provide records of your investigations into media, materials and associated tools, equipment and technology. You can choose your own approach to recording and presenting your findings. Where you have used graphs, charts and diagrams to find out about media and materials, make sure they are included in your presentation. When using technical terms to reflect on your use of media, materials and techniques, you should also use accepted conventions for describing and labelling graphical material.

Your understanding and achievements in Application of Number will be improved if you can explain the effective contribution that numeracy and numerical data make to your research and experiments.

Topic area 3
Designing and making skills

Planning and interpreting information

When designing and making things in art, craft and design you will need to consider three questions very carefully:

- What are you making?
- Why are you making it?
- Who or what are you making it for?

Sometimes you will be expected to work from a given brief; other times you may begin work without any clear guidance. Nevertheless, it will always be necessary at some point to explore:

- The media or materials you are working in
- The techniques or equipment you will need
- The size of any finished artefact
- The costs associated with making it
- What will happen to the final outcome

A given brief will be your first source of relevant information but not the only source. A brief will include constraints and deadlines. These will have an impact on your thinking and developments in terms of costs, materials and timing. You will need to use the full range of interpretive skills including reading and understanding, graphical displays, estimation, observation and preparation of methods and techniques.

Calculating

Depending upon the intended outcomes, working with media and materials will involve calculations to do with dimensions, including area and volume. Other calculations could be to do with your development and production schedule – to make sure you are able to work within the cost constraints and time deadlines.

The amount of calculation will depend upon your intended outcome. The artwork leading to a mural will require the use of scale drawings and calculations on materials and coverage using scale, ratio and proportion. Whereas a sculpture or other 3D design may use a maquette or model and will require work on weight and volume as well as scales and proportion.

Interpreting results and presenting findings

The way you will organise and display your work will depend upon the nature of the final outcome. This will require you to demonstrate that you have worked within the requirements of the brief and have addressed the topic or theme, and worked within the constraints and met the deadlines. You will need to present your calculations or timetable in a chart or table and show the development of your ideas through scale drawings, diagrams or scale models.

Opportunities from optional units

Units with art applications

Collecting information from a variety of sources to help you plan, prepare and begin working in painting, drawing, collage, printmaking, sculpture or installations will require you to explore specialist documents on the skills or techniques associated with these areas. These documents are likely to have information stored in graphs, tables, charts and diagrams that you will need to read and understand.

A variety of simple and complex calculations will be associated with each skill. The extent to which you use them will depend upon the work you undertake. Always try to calculate as well as estimate. Not only will this develop your skill and improve your accuracy, it will also develop your confidence in the importance of number in art.

Units with craft applications

Like the art units, you will have the opportunity to search for information and data from a variety of sources as you develop your ideas and produce finished work. Calculations in craft are usually associated with timing and batch production. This ranges from kiln firing and glaze quality in ceramics to the costs associated with producing and selling items of jewellery or other short-run artefacts.

Units with design applications

There are several types of design: graphics, 3D, surface and textile are perhaps the most common. Each has a range of media, materials and techniques which are relevant to the particular area, and each has a range of technical information and data which will need to be known and understood before undertaking a project in this area.

Calculations will be similar to those associated with art and craft, although they vary according to special areas and will include:

- Amounts and sizes when working on 3D designs for furniture.
- Scales and proportion from graphic and surface design.
- Using formulas for dyes and chemicals in textile and graphic (photo-based) design.

What you must know
Part 1: The Learning Curve will help you with the knowledge you need.

What you must do
Part 2: The Bottom Line will help you with the evidence you need.

Business GNVQ

PART ONE • FOUNDATION • INTERMEDIATE

About the specifications
The Business awards provide you with an opportunity to investigate a range of businesses to help you understand how they work, how they develop and how they are financed.

Topic area 1
Investigating businesses

Planning and interpreting information
Your understanding of business, its functions and aims, will be based on the quality of your research. You will have to identify the sources of relevant information and be able to select and record information. The business activities will vary according to the type of business but you will be expected to find and interpret graphs, tables, charts and diagrams containing information on:

- Products and services
- Ownership and management
- Size in terms of employees and sites
- Income and expenditure
- Shares prices for public companies

You must check that the sources of information are reliable and that the data you have obtained is accurate. You may wish to check accuracy by comparing company reports with newspaper or trade articles or reports.

Calculating
Your understanding of your chosen business will require you to explore the success of its business activities. This will provide you with the opportunity to work with numerical and statistical data as you examine:

- Growth and decline of markets and profitability.
- Profit margins resulting from production and distribution costs as against retail price.
- The impact of distribution costs on price and the importance of location in decisions.
- Investments and share prices of public companies.

Interpreting results and presenting findings
Your numerical and statistical analysis of the businesses you have chosen to investigate will help you to describe and explain how they work. You should present your information graphically wherever possible, using:

See also: **Business Studies GCSE**, page 64

Opportunities

- Charts to show management structures or production schedules.
- Diagrams of production processes or distribution networks.
- Graphs to show the relationship between income and expenditure, or between past and current profit and loss as well as projected performance.

Make sure your calculations, estimations and projections are accurate and sensible. Always check that your presentation and graphics support the points you are trying to make.

Topic area 2
Enterprise and financial literacy

Planning and interpreting information

You will be expected to show awareness of the role of finance in business activity by investigating:

- The different kinds of accounts available to borrowers
- How to borrow money
- How to get the best deal when borrowing
- Your responsibilities as a borrower

You will also have the opportunity to plan and finance a business activity. To do this you will need to understand:

- The range of financial documents used by business
- The means of making payments in business
- How to estimate business costs
- How to project profit or loss
- How to buy and sell in business

Both activities will require you to investigate a range of different sources, including:

- Information from banks and building societies
- Company reports and business management manuals
- Spreadsheets and other financial documents

Calculating

When identifying sources of finance, you will need to carry out a range of calculations involving fractions, decimals and percentages. You will need to understand and calculate compound interest using the appropriate formula. Before deciding on which institution to borrow from, you will need to compare and contrast the range of services they offer, including business start-up benefits, interest rates and other business benefits.

You will be expected to provide calculated estimates of running costs, anticipated income and profit that are supported by a structured business plan. These calculations should cover all the calculation aspects in Application of Number at levels 1 and 2, but any decisions you make must be based on accurate calculations and sensible projections.

Interpreting results and presenting findings

Your presentation will be based on your business plan, your estimated calculations about your business, and your decisions regarding the sources and amounts of finance available. You should select the clearest and most direct way to present your findings. This may include:

- A graph to show projected profitability.
- A chart to show your development process or business plan.
- A diagram or flow chart to show how purchases are made and the documents used.
- A table of sources of income that compares, contrasts and identifies on what basis a source was chosen.

Opportunities from optional units

Sales and customer service

All businesses, whether product-based or service-based, have customers. An analysis of customer services will provide you with a range of data to compare and contrast business performance. Here are some of the apsects to cover:

- Meeting customer expectations
- Securing customer satisfaction
- Protecting customers' rights

The data could be first-hand measurements and observations of different businesses. First it must be collected then it can be analysed. It would be particularly interesting to look at businesses competing for the same customers but in different ways, such as traditional high-street businesses in competition with shopping complexes and web-based services.

What you must know
Part 1: The Learning Curve will help you with the knowledge you need.

What you must do
Part 2: The Bottom Line will help you with the evidence you need.

Construction anf the Built Environment GNVQ

PART ONE • FOUNDATION • INTERMEDIATE

About the specifications

The units of the Construction and Built Environment GNVQ include topics like the study of towns and cities, how buildings are designed and built, and what materials are used. In the optional units you have a choice of studies, such as building design, construction processes, civil engineering, building services and town planning.

Topic area 1
Investigating local areas, buildings and designs

Planning and interpreting information

To investigate the features of your local area and its buildings, you will need to get information and think about how to make best use of it. The following types of activity will produce evidence for the key skill:

- Using maps, plans, technical drawings and sketches.
- Understanding symbols on maps and drawings.
- Using photos, sketches of town features and notes about them.
- Looking up tables and graphs of figures which show changes in a town.
- Looking at building plans and what they are used for.

For level 2 you should use at least one table, chart, diagram or line graph.

Calculating

To make good use of the material you have collected, you will often need to make some calculations. Here are some possible activities connected to the key skill:

- Working with scales and ratios on your maps and drawings.
- Calculating areas of plots of land or areas of rooms.
- Making comparisons between areas such as by a ratio.
- Using statistical data such as numbers of people or changes over time.

Always check your calculations. For level 2 you should show the use of formulas.

Interpreting results and presenting findings

After an investigation you need to show other people your results. You should have a good choice of your investigations and you should have a good choice of opportunities to illustrate your findings, to show trends and to make comparisons. Here are some typical activities:

- Showing information on maps and drawings, by marking copies or by making your own.
- Using labels and correct scales on maps and drawings.
- Using charts and graphs to compre information, e.g. data on recycling or energy use.
- Using graphics to highlight important information from your particular work.

Be able to explain why you think your final results meet the purpose of your investigation, such as changes in land use, or how space is used in a building.

Topic area 2
Construction materials, processes and operations

Planning and interpreting information

There are several units that ask you to find out about building materials, the methods of using them to make buildings, and how people carry out craft operations. You will need information and the following types of activity will produce evidence for the key skill:

- Using technical drawings.
- Looking up properties of materials, such as strength.
- Choosing materials from catalogues and other sources.
- Looking up the costs of materials.
- Looking up schedules or other information about the sequence of jobs.

For level 2 you should use at least one table, chart, diagram or line graph.

Calculating

To make good use of the material you have collected you will often need to make some calculations. Here are some possible activities connected to the key skill:

- Working with scales and ratios on your drawings.
- Calculating the amount of material needed for a job.
- Calculating the costs of materials needed for a job.
- Calculating results from tests you have made on materials.

Always check your calculations. For level 2 you should show the use of formulas.

Interpreting results and presenting findings

After an investigation you need to show other people your results. You should have a good choice of your investigations and you should have a good choice of opportunities to illustrate your findings, to show trends and to make comparisons. Here are some typical activities:

- Showing information on drawings and schedules, such as by marking copies or by making your own.
- Showing data from your tests on materials, such as by using bar charts to compare materials.
- Using graphics to highlight information you think is important.

Be able to explain why you think your final results meet the purpose of your investigation, such as showing the main stages of construction operations.

Engineering GNVQ

PART ONE • FOUNDATION • INTERMEDIATE

About the specifications

The topics in the Engineering GNVQ include engineering design and drawing, investigating the workings of modern engineering products and the making of a product. In the optional units you have a choice of further studies such as engineering maths and science, computing, automation and engineering servicing.

What you must know
Part 1: The Learning Curve will help you with the knowledge you need.

What you must do
Part 2: The Bottom Line will help you with the evidence you need.

Opportunities

EVIDENCE FROM GNVQ COURSES | 89

See also: **Design and Technology GCSE**, page 66

Topic areas 1
Producing a design solution
Investigating new technology products

Planning and interpreting information

To investigate a modern engineering product you will need to get information. Similarly, before you can produce a design solution for someone you need to understand what is wanted and what is available to use in your design. These types of activity will produce evidence for the key skill:

- Reading technical drawings and understanding standard symbols.
- Using product information from manufacturers, such as technical specifications.
- Looking up tables and graphs showing the performance of materials and products.
- Looking up tables and other information giving details of new technology.

For level 2 you should use at least one table, chart, diagram or line graph.

Calculating

To make good use of the material you have collected, you will need to make calculations. Here are some possible activities connected to the key skill:

- Working with scales and ratios on your drawings.
- Calculating areas and volumes of materials and components.
- Using statistical data such as numbers of people working in an engineering sector.
- Calculating or comparing the results of tests on products and materials.
- Calculating savings in materials, in time and costs.
- Calculating performance figures and energy consumption.
- Comparing numbers, such as by using ratios.

Always check your calculations. For level 2 you should show the use of formulas.

Interpreting results and presenting findings

To show the results of your work to other people, you need to select suitable pieces of information and make them look good. This is especially true when you have produced a particular design and need to persuade other people that it is a good one. Here are some typical activities:

- Showing information by drawings and sketches.
- Using drawing techniques to present a final design solution.
- Using labels and correct scales on drawings.
- Using charts and graphs to compare information, such as figures for costs, time and labour involved in new technology products.
- Using graphics to highlight important information from your particular work.

Be able to explain why you think your final results meet the purpose of your work, such as satisfying the design brief.

Topic area 2
Making a product

Planning and interpreting information

There are several units that involve making or servicing engineering products. These activities are planned by using a production plan, following a service schedule and setting up equipment. They provide the following sort of opportunities for the key skill:

- Creating a production plan (level 2)
- Reading a production plan
- Reading information from drawings
- Looking up sizes and qualities of materials
- Setting up equipment such as scales and settings
- Taking measurements as you work

For level 2 you should use at least one table, chart, diagram or line graph.

Calculating

Here are some calculations that can be used for evidence:

- Working out measurements from drawings
- Calculating the amount of material needed
- Calculating the costs of materials
- Adjusting equipment settings while removing material

Always check your calculations. For level 2 you should show the use of formulas. You may do some of these calculations while carrying out a process, so make sure that you keep a record, perhaps in a notebook.

Interpreting results and presenting findings

At level 2 you need to produce your own production plan and will have the opportunity to use charts and diagrams to show the processes used and the order in which they are carried out.

What you must know
Part 1: The Learning Curve will help you with the knowledge you need.

What you must do
Part 2: The Bottom Line will help you with the evidence you need.

Health and Social Care GNVQ
PART ONE • FOUNDATION • INTERMEDIATE

About the specifications

The Health and Social Care awards include topics on the sector itself, on promoting health and well-being and on personal development and relationships. For Part One you need only concentrate on the three mandatory units – topic areas 1, 2 and 3.

Topic area 1
Health and well-being

Planning and interpreting information

You can establish the health of a person by using information taken from equipment that often gives numerical readings. You will have a clear purpose (trying to establish the health and well-being of the person) and the equipment could be helping to establish weight, height, body mass, and/or the pulse rate and the recovery rate after exercise. Taking the same measures over time will also allow you to make comparisons and monitor changes. This will involve more numerical information and some calculations and it will enable you to construct tables or graphs. Working with diet sheets and dealing with food energy values are further opportunities to handle numerical information.

Calculating

Body mass index (BMI) is calculated by dividing a person's weight in kilos by the square of their height in metres. In collecting information about height, weight or BMI for larger groups of people (at least 20) it would be possible to work out different averages (mean, mode, median) for the group. Remember, when dealing with groups of people and looking at something like BMI, it will be important to be tactful and it will be a good opportunity to show that you can deal with this type of information and situation sensitively during the report-writing stage.

You might like to look at and compare the range of readings and measurements that are present when looking at males and females as separate categories. You could also explore the changes in spread of readings when looking at different age groups. Looking at the range of actual height readings within an age set might produce some interesting statistics; for example, within adolescents looking at 10–12 year olds and comparing the results with those of 14–16 year olds.

Interpreting results and presenting findings

Showing the results of measurements taken on large groups offers some straightforward opportunities to present information graphically. Bar charts would be a useful way of doing this. You could put the range of possible heights on an increasing scale along the x-axis and the numbers of students on the y-axis. This will also allow you to show that you can round measurements appropriately and present numerical information using appropriate scales.

Topic area 2
Doing some research in health and social care

Planning and interpreting information

To carry out any research project you need to be able to identify relevant data, collect and interpret data and analyse your results. This will give lots of opportunities to generate Application of Number evidence. You could be collecting information first-hand by making observations, creating questionnaires or doing a survey, and you could be adding to what you are finding out by looking at secondary sources of information too. Perhaps you will only look at secondary sources, but you will still have an opportunity to use numbers. Secondary sources give you a great opportunity to show you can interpret information correctly. Try to concentrate on the secondary sources that use numbers, perhaps looking at tables, charts and graphs.

Using quantitative research methods is an obvious way to ensure you are creating data that could easily be written up as numerical information and presented graphically. If you are going to carry out research, take some time to look at the different quantitative research methods you could try.

Calculating

Once you have collected data from your various sources, you will have opportunities to do a variety of different calculations. If you are trying to get level 1 in Application of Number, try to collect responses to questionnaires or surveys of at least 10 people. For level 2 try to get responses from 20 people. For both levels this is one of your best chances of showing you can work with large sets of data and can compare results.

Depending on what you have been researching, you might have an opportunity to demonstrate these skills at level 1:

- Find the average (mean) of up to 10 items.
- Find the range for up to 10 items.
- Show you understand simple percentages.

Try to demonstrate these skills at level 2:

- Carry out calculations involving two or more steps, (e.g. for a pie chart).
- Convert measurements between systems (e.g. from imperial to metric).
- Compare sets of data with a minimum of 20 items.

Interpreting results and presenting findings

There will be lots of ways of presenting the information you have found out through your research. Remember to make sure that you have labelled the information you present as a graph or chart correctly. If you have collected the information yourself, it would be a shame not to present it correctly.

Remember to write down why you have chosen any scales you have used giving good reasons why they were the best choice. When taking measurements for health care, the differences between people or measurements can be small. If you use too small a scale, your graph or chart will look dull and boring and, more importantly, it will be hard to read. So pick a scale that helps the reader see the differences you want to show.

Topic area 3
Health, social care and early years provision (investigating the sector)

When looking at the health and social care sector, you might have to deal with numbers like these:

- How many people are employed in the sector (this could involve having to round numbers and make approximations).
- How much the local authority and/or national government spends on health care.
- The contribution the sector makes to the local or national economy.

If you make comparisons or look at changes in the figures over a period of time, there will be lots of opportunities to interpret, calculate and present this information.

At level 2 you could also track the sector's performance on the stock market. Look at the Business signposts and the Leisure and Tourism signposts and see the the chapter on Evidence from everyday sources for guidance on how to do this and the number work that is involved.

Other foundation opportunities

Investigating common hazards and health emergencies

You may have to look at environmental safety surveys and audits. This could involve looking at data in tables, charts or graphs. You may have an opportunity to explore a place of work and record the various safety features; for example, you could survey the number of fire extinguishers in a workplace (taking note of the types of fire they are designed to tackle – electrical, chemical etc,).

Different fires need to be extinguished by different types of fire extinguisher. Make sure you know how to choose the right one; for example, you should never use water on an electrical fire. You could present this information using a bar chart. You could also use a pie chart to show the shares for the different fire extinguishers out of the total number of fire extinguishers. Look at the numbers that appear on fire extinguishers and see if there are other opportunities to create Application of Number evidence.

If you are looking at risk assessments or safety audits, you may have the opportunity to work with plans or layouts of buildings. This might be a good chance to show that you can work with straightforward scales.

Planning diets

This could involve working to budgets. You could use graphical methods like pie charts or bar charts to show how you spent the money in producing a meal, or even show where the money for only one course went. At a greater level of detail, and slightly more difficult to calculate or work out, you could show how a balanced diet could be displayed graphically, indicating the correct proportions of protein, carbohydrate and fat. Also take time to look at how many numbers and calculations appear on food labels and packaging. You could interpret this information and find ways of presenting it using charts and other graphic methods.

Other intermediate opportunities

When doing intermediate optional units you don't need to worry about showing you can work with more difficult number calculations. You need to keep working at the level 2 standard and look for more opportunities to generate evidence.

You might be able to do some more research that will create number opportunities. There will certainly be more opportunities to learn about physiology and health care. This will mean more opportunities to take measurements and to do calculations and present data.

You will find that you have an opportunity to study the social care sector in more detail and this could involve learning about how the sector is financed. This will involve working with number as well.

What you must know
Part 1: The Learning Curve will help you with the knowledge you need.

What you must do
Part 2: The Bottom Line will help you with the evidence you need.

Hospitality and Catering GNVQ

PART ONE • FOUNDATION • INTERMEDIATE

About the specifications
The Hospitality and Catering awards include the study of food and drink, accommodation and front office and practical investigations of hospitality and catering outlets and industries. There will be opportunities to specialise a little in particular aspects of hospitality and catering that interest you. Most units should provide you with an opportunity to generate some of your Application of Number evidence. For Part One you need only concentrate on the three mandatory units – topic areas 1, 2 and 3.

Topic area 1
Investigations into hospitality and catering industries or particular outlets

Planning and interpreting information
Here are the types of opportunity that might exist when you study this topic:

- Looking at data on the size of the industry
- Looking at how much money the industry makes
- Working out how many people are employed
- Working with government statistics

Calculating
When investigating a local hospitality and catering industry, you could compare it with other local industries or compare your local area with the national industry in general. This will give you the opportunity to work with numbers as you look at the different percentage contributions the hospitality and catering industry makes locally compared to others.

For example, you could compare the financial contribution hospitality and catering makes to the local economy, comparing it with other import-

ant local sectors and look at the importance in terms of numbers employed. Having looked at local comparisons, you could look at how hospitality and catering locally compares with the national contribution.

This will mean working with percentages in terms of the different contributions and calculating how to turn these percentages into different parts of a pie chart or how to present your findings as a chart or table. Or it might be restricted to looking at just two local outlets, using simple bar charts to present your findings.

Interpreting results and presenting findings

You will have the opportunity to show that you can select methods of presenting information by selecting appropriate graphs, charts or tables. This could also help you show that you can use investigative skills effectively in finding out information about hospitality and catering.

Topic area 2
Preparing and providing food for customers

Planning and interpreting information

Here are some good sources of numerical information for hospitality and catering:

- Instruments for measuring and weighing, like scales and timers, measuring in everyday units like litres and grams; using measuring jugs.
- Numerical information found in recipes, e.g. quantities of ingredients and cooking times.
- Numerical information found on food packaging, e.g. typical values of energy, fibre, fat; amounts per serving and amounts per 100 grams; kilojoules, (kJ) and kilocalories (calories).
- Costs and prices, differences between wholesale and retail prices, etc.

Calculating

Calculating opportunities include:

- Conversions from metric to imperial or vice versa
- Conversions from gas to electric or vice versa, e.g. when cooking
- Calculating costs and working with budgets

Interpreting results and presenting findings

You could present information based on some of the numbers you have been working with using charts and tables. Though this may not be asked for directly in your hospitality and catering course evidence, it may help to enhance the quality of your work and show your activities and investigations more clearly. It is also worth thinking about how customer bills could be presented graphically to show how the charges were made up. There are several different ways this could be done.

Topic area 3
Investigating accommodation and front office services

Planning and interpreting information

You may have an opportunity to work with customer bills and payments that will involve working with numbers. This will provide opportunities to work with some straightforward numerical information.

Calculating

By looking at residential and non-residential outlets, you could look at comparing the different sources of income and expenditure in general terms. Having found out the numerical information needed for this, you could then turn the information into two pie charts which will help show the different income and expenditure patterns clearly.

Interpreting results and presenting findings

Pie charts are useful ways of presenting any comparisons clearly. You may also consider using a stack chart, where the residential outlet is one stack and the non-residential outlet is the other. Like pie charts, you would first need to establish what different percentage contributions make up the income and expenditure of each outlet. Presenting any information comparing residential and non-residential outlets as simple bar charts might be a more straightforward way of doing this comparison at level 1.

Further opportunities for evidence

Exploring restaurants

Learning how to prepare bills for customers and calculate the charges for typical meals, then calculating VAT and service charges are all good activities for collecting Application of Number evidence. You may even be able to work out average prices of meals in different types of restaurant, or calculate the average costs of different food courses. One useful activity is looking at typical bills and using a chart to show how the bill can be broken down into the different costs. For example, you could present a bill graphically using a bar chart to show the amount spent on the starter, then the main course, then the dessert, adding in drinks, service charges or other charges that occur. Presenting this information as a pie chart would be a little more complicated but would provide another good opportunity for number evidence.

Planning diets

When looking at diets and producing healthy diets, you will get the opportunity to read and interpret typical values of food. This will bring in working with calories as well as the different percentages of protein, fibre, fat, etc. Have a look at the packaging on food and see the different numbers and calculations that are on display. This does not only happen for individual foods.

You could work out in your dietary work how much fat, protein and

carbohydrate should be present in a diet. Alternatively, you could work out what contribution any meal you prepare or recommend makes to healthy daily totals of nutrients.

A simple exercise would be to take a tin of beans or a packet of cereal (or any other food that is labelled with the right information), look at the tables showing the typical values then work out how you could present this information using charts. Perhaps you could draw bar charts showing the different proportions of protein, carbohydrate, fat, fibre and sodium.

Another simple excise would be to draw a graph that shows the amount of calories in different servings. You could put the number of servings along the x-axis and the number of calories along the y-axis. This information is often available on food labels or packaging.

Information and Communication Technology GNVQ

PART ONE • FOUNDATION • INTERMEDIATE

About the specifications
The Information and Communication Technology (ICT) awards include the study of topics like presenting and handling information and product design.

Topic area 1
Handling information

Planning and interpreting information
You will be expected to create and produce documents in a variety of layouts and styles that meet a clear purpose. Many of the documents will need to depend upon information drawn from databases and spreadsheets. You will need to be able to:

- Identify sources of information.
- Find relevant information from the sources (e.g. databases, the internet, transport timetables and instrumentation manuals).
- Sort, classify and format information (using operations such as equal to, less than or greater than).
- Store information (using integers, decimals, common measures or formulas).

In addition to using these sources, make sure you can accurately read the charts and graphs you are working with. Remember that electronic evidence is as valid as hard-copy evidence but it should be recorded.

Calculating

The handling techniques you will use will depend upon the task or project. Numerical information is now commonly found in spreadsheets (which are really number-structured databases). A spreadsheet can be used to store information about salaries, price structures, loans and mortgages, or materials and quantities. Each type of information provides opportunities for you to work with:

- Amounts and sizes
- Scales and proportion
- Statistics
- Formulas

Interpreting results and presenting findings

Once you have set up your database or spreadsheet you will have access to all the data that it holds. You will also be able to use your processing skills to explore, predict and present additional information. Make sure that when you present numerical data using graphs, charts and diagrams, you use established conventions for titles, labels and scales. Always select ways of presenting information that help you to explain your findings. Never use the technology to produce graphics just because they look good – they must mean something too!

Topic area 2
Product design

Planning and interpreting information

When designing and carrying out an ICT project you will need to answer these three questions:

- What are you making?
- Why are you making it?
- What is its purpose or function?

You will be expected to explore a range of different sources to help you draw up a list of projects and prepare information on resources required. This will involve you in:

- Obtaining information from written and graphical material.
- Reading and understanding graphs, tables, charts and diagrams.
- Selecting methods, including grouping data.

The success of your approach will be measured by the quality of your project proposal and the planning and preparation that support it.

Calculating

Your calculations will depend upon the focus of the project itself but they are likely to include:

- Amounts and sizes
- Scales and proportion
- Handling statistics

Opportunities to use formulas will be found if you set up automated routines. Make sure that calculations are accurate. Whenever errors are identified, ensure the calculations are corrected and then systematically tested.

Interpreting results and presenting findings

The evaluation of your product offers you the opportunity to explain how it meets the original design specification. You may also have the opportunity to produce scale diagrams and graphs or charts to provide details and specifications of your product.

Opportunities from optional units

Presenting information

ICT provides you with a range of opportunities to produce:

- Numerical tables
- Graphs, including histograms and bar graphs
- Charts, including pie charts
- Diagrams, including scale and schematic diagrams

Most ICT software now provides applications that enable numerical data to be translated into graphical form. The ability to use ICT in this way is not an adequate demonstration of Application of Number. You must ensure that established conventions, including scales and labels, are appropriate and that you can understand and explain your choice of presentational techniques.

Land and Environment GNVQ

PART ONE • FOUNDATION • INTERMEDIATE

About the specifications

The Land and Environment awards include the study of topics like caring for animals and plants, investigating environmental factors and investigating the land and environment sector.

Topic area 1
Investigating environmental factors and looking at ecosystems

Planning and interpreting information

When looking at ecology as a topic you will be learning how to measure and record factors like:

- Rainfall
- Light intensity
- Wind speed and direction, soil and air temperature
- Humus, nitrogen, potash and phosphate levels in soil

What you must know
Part 1: The Learning Curve will help you with the knowledge you need.

What you must do
Part 2: The Bottom Line will help you with the evidence you need.

- Soil pH

There will also be opportunities to record the distribution of plant and animal species in a habitat.

Ecology involves collecting a range of different numbers and numerical information first-hand by measuring and observing. There might also be opportunities to read appropriate numerical information from charts and tables.

Some of the measurements (like weather) may have to be taken over a longer period, perhaps two weeks. You could look at a map and gauge the size of the area that you will be studying.

Calculating

When taking your measurements you will need to work out what would be an appropriate level of accuracy for your results. Doing a survey can often mean converting between fractions, decimals and percentages; for example, working out what percentage of the seven blackbirds recorded was female.

Depending on the results of your survey, you might have the opportunity to work with sets of data with a minimum of 20 items. One idea would be to focus on a single common species of plant or animal and take a number of more accurate physical measurements (e.g. length, leaf variations) and then compare the data by working out the different averages (mean and mode). You could also use range to describe the spread within the sets. This will also involve working with a greater degree of accuracy to allow you to detect the variations.

Working with maps will involve working out dimensions from scale drawings, as well as approximating areas.

Interpreting results and presenting findings

There will be several different opportunities to present the results of your environmental measurements. These will range from tables or spreadsheets to charts and graphs. Rainfall, temperature and species numbers can all be measured over time and may be clearly and effectively presented as a graph.

You can look at categories of animals like birds, and present the number of each bird type seen as a pie chart (e.g. out of the 15 birds seen, 4 were blackbirds, 1 was a thrush, 2 were robins, 4 were chaffinches and 4 were crows). At a simpler level you could present the number of types of animals seen.

You may want to present your area studied as a scale drawing. This will involve taking measurements and then drawing themaccurately to scale.

Topic area 2
Caring for plants

Planning and interpreting information
You may have to work with instrumentation to interpret and record:

- Light
- Temperature
- Water
- Levels of nitrogen, phosphate and potash
- pH levels

Packaging for fertiliser or chemicals carries information on weight, percentage values of ingredients and amounts to be used per area of land. On a smaller scale, most plant food has detailed information about:

- Ratios and proportions to be used when it is dissolved in water; these might change with the solution volume, the application frequency and the plant type.
- How many grams to be used per square metre, or ounces per square yard; this involves working out areas and volumes, converting measurements, etc.
- Analysis of ingredients (e.g. total nitrogen and other elements used); this might involve converting between fractions, decimals and percentages.

Calculating

When looking at husbandry systems look out for opportunities to work with numbers in explaining yields, production levels and input levels of fertilisers and agrochemicals. With fertilisers and chemicals you could look at the amounts and how much land they can cover. This will mean working with areas and units of measurement, for the amounts of fertiliser and chemicals used, and for the number of acres they can be used on. This will involve conversion of measurements between systems like number of kilos per acre, and it will involve working out areas and volumes.

Plant food often involves working out the number of millilitres (ml) of food to the number of litres of water (proportions and ratios). This can be converted into imperial measures (fluid ounces, pints and gallons). You may have an opportunity to grow plants and experiment with growth rates and yields depending on whether fertiliser or plant food is used. This will allow large sets of data to be collected based on your measurements. This will then allow you to find out averages (mean and mode) and work out ranges to describe the spread within your sets of data. You will also have to be precise in measuring out the different types or strengths of fertiliser or plant food.

Interpreting results and presenting findings

You could convert the information on the ingredients of plant food (normally given in percentages) into a pie chart. You could create a conversion table for dealing with metric and imperial measurements to help others judge how much of something to use. Data from plant growth experiments can be presented using charts, tables and graphs.

Further opportunities for evidence

Growing plants
Other potential opportunities will involve working with numbers and calculations associated with costs and budgets, sales and profits.

Caring for animals
Working with animal measurements will provide opportunities for Application of Number evidence, as will learning about husbandry and looking at production, costs associated with feed, relationships between feeding, production and relevant environmental factors. There may also be opportunities to measure and monitor changes in environmental factors.

Taking part in an enterprise
You are likely to be involved with income and expenditure, looking at set-up and running costs, monitoring sales, and calculating break-even point and profit. Much of this information could be presented using different graphical methods in a company or enterprise report. There will also be market research to carry out and results to analyse and present.

What you must know
Part 1: The Learning Curve will help you with the knowledge you need.

What you must do
Part 2: The Bottom Line will help you with the evidence you need.

Leisure and Tourism GNVQ
PART ONE • FOUNDATION • INTERMEDIATE

About the specifications
The Leisure and Tourism awards include the study of topics like investigating the leisure and tourism sectors and marketing and promotion.

Topic area 1
Investigating the leisure and tourism sectors

Planning and interpreting information
The national government and local government, as well as market research agencies produce a number of different sources of information that show information like:

- Estimated attendance for different tourist attractions.
- Leisure and tourism's contribution to the local and national economies.
- The number of people employed in the industries.
- Increases in visitors, numbers employed or money made over a period of time.

All of these statistics will also involve different ways of rounding numbers and approximating.

Broadsheet newspapers carry financial information on the performance of leisure and hotel stocks and shares. You could invest an imaginary amount of money in your sector; choose your companies and see how well they perform over a certain length of time (perhaps a month). This will allow you to interpret the information about the shares as they appear in the newspaper, then invest your money and calculate how well it is doing; plot it on a graph.

Alternatively, you could track performance of just one company over the course of a month, checking the share price once or twice a week. Remember, though, at level 1 finding the share price would be sufficient evidence to show you could read these sorts of tables. At level 2 it would be sufficient to plot the share price changes on a graph, based on your interpretation of the data in the financial section of a newspaper.

Calculating

If you are going to research the contribution that the sector makes to the local and/or national economy, you may have to interpret government statistics or statistics based on your area. Very often this type of information comes in tables or in graphs and charts.

Working with shares will give you a number of opportunities to calculate at level 2. You can work out the percentage increase or decrease of the share prices, or how much money could have been made or lost had you bought some shares and sold them a month later.

If you are able to get hold of your local council information about how they spend local government money on leisure and tourism related projects, you will be able to perform several different types of calculations. You can compare this spending to spending in other areas.

Interpreting results and presenting findings

All the suggestions above will create opportunities to present your work using different graphical methods. You will also have an opportunity to select methods that are more effective and appropriate than others. Some of the suggestions will allow you to create graphs that show trends you may have found, e.g. increases in the number employed in the sector.

The performance of a company's shares over a period of time, e.g. a month, could be shown using a graph or bar chart with the price as the y-axis and when you checked their value (e.g. week 1, week 2) as the x-axis. This type of approach will also show that you can work out appropriate scales and work to appropriate degrees of accuracy.

Topic area 2
Marketing and promotion

Planning and interpreting information

If you are working with data from market research, you will find opportunities to look at how different types of data can be presented and opportunities to show that you understand the data. You may even have the opportunity to generate information from conducting your own market research.

Whether you decide to carry out your own survey, make observations or construct a questionnaire, you will be generating information that can be turned into numerical information and used to back up any points you need to make. In carrying out market research you will also need to develop a clear purpose. This will also establish a purpose for your Application of Number key skill.

Target marketing can take you into greater detail by looking at how different categories respond to your research, categories like:

- Age
- Gender
- Social group
- Lifestyle
- Ethnicity

This type of information can be used to spot patterns or trends within the overall information.

Calculating
Price as an element of the marketing mix can lead to you working with calculations relating to:

- The organisation's costs
- What customers will pay
- What the market will tolerate

This brings in:

- What competitors are charging
- The required profit margin

Price can also involve calculations relating to peak and off-peak rates (you could show the changes in the rates as a percentage), to high season and low season, as well as discounts and special offers.

Promotion as an element of the marketing mix can involve considering costs which can be influenced by:

- The amount of promotional space
- The frequency of the promotion
- The size of the audience

You could look at prices involved in using the local newspaper as a means of promotion, producing a report on the different costs. By looking at different newspapers there will be an opportunity for comparisons and establishing which might be the better value. You would also need to consider the size of the audience.

Interpreting results and presenting findings
Pie charts and stack charts are useful ways of showing how the total price of something is broken down into different parts. Results of surveys can be presented in several different ways. If you have looked at the different responses made by different groups to particular questions,

then charts and diagrams will prove to be a good way of getting this complex information over to the reader. This will be a good opportunity to show that you can select appropriate methods to present your information.

Topic area 3
Travel and holidays

Planning and interpreting information

Guidebooks often have information about average daily hours of sunshine, average monthly rainfall and average monthly temperature. Humidity may also be a factor in some parts of the world. This usually appears as a chart or a table. You will also find this information in many travel brochures. Depending on the destination, the charts or graphs may record negative numbers.

In a few instances the temperature graph can look quite complicated with an x-axis showing months, a left-hand y-axis showing temperature in Celsius and a right-hand y-axis showing the temperature in Fahrenheit. The same might also be true of rainfall, where the two y-axes could be used for millimetres and inches.

Calculating

Reading, understanding and calculating play a big part in trying to obtain the price of a holiday these days. Just look at all the work involved in trying to find out the actual price of a holiday using a holiday brochure (see page 134 for an example of what can be done using a page from a travel brochure).

Currency conversions are another obvious source of calculations. This is a way of converting between two systems. For European destinations you can even put in a third by showing the value in euros.

Time differences may also be a useful source of straightforward calculations. This can become more appropriate as key skill number evidence if you are calculating travel times along with presenting information about the relevant local departure and arrival times. Remember that crossing time zones makes this a little more complicated. For example, on a seven-hour flight to New York, you could leave London at 1400 hours and arrive in New York at 1600 hours. If you take the three-hour Concorde flight, you would leave London at 1400 hours and arrive in New York at 1200 hours on the same day. Why don't the numbers add up? Because New York is five hours behind London.

Interpreting results and presenting findings

There are several ways to present information to potential tourists. You can make your own mind up about what you think is the most effective way to present average hours of sunshine, temperatures and rainfall, based on your own experience of looking at travel brochures and books. Most will be using graphical methods. Simple graphs can then be constructed to quickly help you convert between two currencies.

Plugging gaps in your evidence

Work out the area of a sports pitch (work out areas of simple rectangular spaces); this is a level 1 opportunity. The following examples are a mix of levels 1 and 2:

- Work out the area of the centre circle on a football pitch and compare it to the area of the whole pitch. This could be shown as a ratio or even as a pie chart with the area of the pitch as the whole pie chart and the area of the centre circle as a shaded area on the pie chart.
- You could work out the area of the try-scoring area compared to the pitch size on a rugby field.
- You could also compare the size of a singles tennis court to a doubles tennis court.

What you must know
Part 1: The Learning Curve will help you with the knowledge you need.

What you must do
Part 2: The Bottom Line will help you with the evidence you need.

Manufacturing GNVQ

PART ONE • FOUNDATION • INTERMEDIATE

About the specifications

The topics in the Manufacturing GNVQ include investigating how companies use new technology to make products. In other units you develop your skills of designing and making products. The optional units give you a choice of further studies in manufacturing, such as computing, automation and quality control.

Topic areas 1
Investigating new technology in manufacturing
Working with a design brief

Planning and interpreting information

To investigate modern manufacturing you will need to get information about products and companies. Similarly, before you can produce a design solution for someone you need to understand what is available for use in your design. Here are some types of activity that will produce the evidence you need:

- Using information about companies and their sectors.
- Looking up the stages and activities for manufacturing a product.
- Looking up tables and other information giving details of new technology.
- Using product information from manufacturers, such as technical specifications.
- Looking up tables and graphs showing the performance of materials and products.

See also: **Design and Technology**, page 66

Opportunities

For level 2 you should use at least one table, chart, diagram or line graph.

Calculating

To make good use of the material you have collected you will need to make calculations. Here are some possible activities connected to the key skill:

- Working with scales and ratios on your drawings.
- Calculating areas and volumes of materials and components.
- Using statistical data such as numbers of people working in a manufacturing sector.
- Calculating material usage, production time and production costs.
- Calculating production details and constraints which affect the design.
- Comparing numbers, such as by using ratios.

Always check your calculations. For level 2 you should show the use of formulas.

Interpreting results and presenting findings

To show the results of your work to other people you need to select useful information and present it effectively. This is especially true when you have produced a particular design and need to persuade other people that it is a good one. Here are some typical activities:

- Showing information by sketches, drawings and other graphical methods.
- Presenting a final design solution, using drawing techniques with correct scales.
- Preparing mock-ups, models or prototypes with correct scales.
- Using charts and graphs to compare information about manufacturing new technology products.
- Using graphics to highlight important information from your particular work.

Be able to explain why you think your final results meet the purpose of your work, such as satisfying the design brief.

Topic area 2
Making a product

Planning and interpreting information

When making a product you will be using a manufacturing schedule and whatever materials and equipment are needed for your chosen product. These activities provide the following sort of opportunities for the key skill:

- Creating a manufacturing schedule (level 2)
- Using a manufacturing schedule
- Looking up sizes and qualities of materials

- Setting up equipment such as scales and settings
- Taking measurements as you work (e.g. size or weight)

For level 2 you should use at least one table, chart, diagram or line graph.

Calculating

Here are some calculations that may be used for evidence:

- Working out measurements from drawings
- Calculating the amount of material needed
- Calculating the costs of materials
- Calculating quantities required for batches of product (level 2)
- Adjusting equipment settings while removing material

Always check your calculations. For level 2 you should show the use of formulas. You may do some of these calculations while carrying out a process, so make sure that you keep a record, perhaps in a notebook.

Interpreting results and presenting findings

At level 2 you need to produce your own manufacturing schedule and you will have the opportunity to use charts and diagrams to show the processes used and the order in which they are carried out.

What you must know
Part 1: The Learning Curve will help you with the knowledge you need.

What you must do
Part 2: The Bottom Line will help you with the evidence you need.

Media: Communication and Production GNVQ

PART ONE • FOUNDATION • INTERMEDIATE

About the specifications

The Media awards include the development of investigation and production skills.

Topic area 1
Investigating media industries and products

Planning and interpreting information

The media industry is a large and diverse industry ranging from traditional text-based communications to the latest interactive digital communications technology. Any investigation of this industry will provide a wealth of information from a range of different sources, both written and graphical. Numerical information can be found on:

- Audience demands within each part of the industry
- Scale of audiences for different media products
- The profitability of different media companies

Further information can be drawn from first-hand observation using data collection techniques such as questionnaires.

Calculating

Your calculations will depend upon the focus of your activity but investigation of the industry will require you to compare the performance of different parts. By isolating the data collected on different parts of the industry you can produce graphics, charts and diagrams which compare:

- Audience figures for different products, e.g. theatre and film.
- Expenditure on promotion and marketing for theatre, film, etc.
- The income, profitability and circulation of different companies, e.g. newspapers and magazines.

These graphical formats can be used to show:

- Average receipts
- Profitability margins
- Percentage increase in audience figures

Interpreting results and presenting findings

The graphical formats used to identify performances of different media industries will provide a basis for you to present your findings. They can be included in reports or oral presentations of your findings. Always make sure that your presentation and results support what you say about different parts of the industry.

Topic area 2
Production skills

Media communications require many different skills, including:

- Video and photography
- Sound production
- Publishing
- Multimedia

You will be required to select one or more areas to investigate, then plan and develop the skills that show you are developing good working practices and skills.

Planning and interpreting information

The technical aspects of your skills development will come from two different sources:

- Instruction manuals containing written and graphical material
- First-hand observation and following instructions given by others

You will be expected to interpret graphs, tables, charts and diagrams to develop an understanding of how to operate technology and develop new techniques.

Calculating

In media your calculations will depend upon your chosen areas of skill development. For example:

- **Video and photography**: during image production you will need to calculate power needs based on the area of the location.
- **Sound systems**: during recording sessions you will need to work with scales and proportions when dealing with timing and sound levels.
- **Publishing**: during page layout you will need to work with a range of different scales and measurements.
- **Multimedia**: during the development of interactive products you may need to understand and use a range of statistical data on audience needs and reactions, to support the development process.

Interpreting results and presenting findings

Presenting your work is a natural part of media. Make sure that your skill development is clearly recorded by notes and records on the outcomes themselves. When presenting, make sure to choose methods that use your improved skills and relate them to the original area of development such as sound or video.

Topic area 3
Working to a brief

Planning and interpreting Information

The skills you use when working to a media brief are very similar to those in art and design. The brief is a source of relevant information but it is only one source. You will need to:

- Research the brief fully, including any interviews and surveys, to establish demand or need for the product from the target audience.
- Identify the equipment needed and any associated costs.
- Draw up a production plan that includes a development schedule.

Calculating

Whatever the product or artefact you produce, you must be able to justify demand or need and provide detailed and accurate costs:

- The data you have collected from surveys, interviews or other sources can be grouped to show audience or user responses or reactions.
- The costs associated with development, production and promotion can be prepared using a balance sheet.

Interpreting results and presenting findings

You will be expected to present your product or artefact to the client and explain how it meets the original brief. You may wish to use:

- Tables and charts to show audience and user responses.
- Graphs to show development costs and scales of production.
- Diagrams to show the production or development process.

Make sure that your presentation is supported by the information you have collected and the calculations you have made.

What you must know
Part 1: The Learning Curve will help you with the knowledge you need.

What you must do
Part 2: The Bottom Line will help you with the evidence you need.

Opportunities

Performing Arts GNVQ

About the specifications

The Performing Arts awards include the study of topics like exploring opportunities in performing arts, skills development and performing work. Most of your opportunities for generating evidence for Application of Number may have to come from working with audience statistics, with surveys or with money and budgets. It will be difficult to use your actual performing as a means of generating number evidence. However, focusing on audience surveys and money and budgets will help you to develop a fuller appreciation of what performing arts and the entertainment industries are all about. For Part One you need only concentrate on the three mandatory units – topic areas 1, 2 and 3.

Topic area 1
Opportunities in performing arts

Planning and interpreting information

There could be an opportunity to do a little research into audience or user statistics for performances or events. You could be looking at the types of people who attend different performances and events, or trying to gauge an audience's reactions to a performance. You might even be doing a survey of residents' opinions on the local performing arts and entertainment industry resources or amenities in your area. All these examples will allow you to work with numbers. Information that you generate or collect yourself will count as primary information. You should also try to use information from other sources (secondary information) to help support your work.

Calculating

Once you have collected statistics you will be able to use them in different ways. You can work out the responses people made to questions, showing them as percentages. When people have expressed a range of attitudes, you could show this by presenting your results as a pie chart.

Interpreting results and presenting findings

The data you collect yourself and the statistics you obtain from other sources, both can be presented graphically. You will have opportunities to demonstrate that you can select appropriate methods to show the data.

You might be interested in doing some research into local government, national government or even lottery funding of the different arts and entertainment industries. This will involve working with figures and it will provide opportunities to show that you can select the information you need from secondary sources, you can work with the statistics you have obtained, and you can select and use appropriate presentation methods like graphs, charts and tables.

Other similar ideas that you could consider researching are employment patterns in the industry and the contribution the industry makes to the local or national economy. Again, there will be opportunities to present your findings using charts, tables and diagrams.

Topic area 2
Arts administration and marketing

Planning and interpreting information
There might be an opportunity to look at a venue's budget, to look at the budget for a show, or even to work with a budget from a production that you will be involved with.

Calculating
Pie charts can be useful ways of explaining how the budget was spent. The total budget makes up the complete chart and each area of expenditure will make up a piece of the chart. This will involve making calculations that will involve two or more steps and also working with ratios and proportions. Selling tickets and recording takings may lead you to investigate break-even points and profit margins. Handling money and preparing budgets are two more related aspects.

Interpreting results and presenting findings
Many people find budgets or other financial information confusing. You will have an opportunity to show that you can use appropriate graphical methods to communicate this type of information clearly. This will help others understand what the budget was spent on.

Topic area 3
Promoting, organising and evaluating events

Planning and interpreting information
Working with budgets for promotion or for the entire event will involve dealing with promotion, refreshment and materials budgets. When preparing for an event, you will have opportunities for working in the box office and with ticket selling, including records of sales.

Calculating
When it comes to evaluating the success of an event, you can look at how financially successful it was. Although you might not be aiming for a profit, you might still want to break even. You could provide a detailed breakdown of where money was made and spent across the range of different sources of income and expenditure.

There are also the other ways of evaluating the success of the event. You may wish to take audience attitude surveys, gauging reactions to the performance and/or facilities made available. This may involve making

questionnaires, then using the results of the questionnaires (your findings) to produce numerical information. Looking at a large number of audience responses to surveys or questionnaires will allow you to work out the average response to individual questions. You may also be able to show that you can work out the different types of average (mean, mode and median).

When working with money and budgets, pie charts can be a good way of presenting information on how income was made (if there were different sources of income) or different types of expenditure. Converting the financial information you have on income and expenditure into data for a pie chart will mean doing calculations.

Interpreting results and presenting findings
You will be able to present the results of your audience surveys or questionnaires graphically. Depending on what questions you ask you will have a choice of different types of charts or diagrams.

What you must know
Part 1: The Learning Curve will help you with the knowledge you need.

What you must do
Part 2: The Bottom Line will help you with the evidence you need.

Retail and Distributive Services GNVQ

PART ONE • FOUNDATION • INTERMEDIATE

About the specifications
The Retail and Distributive Services awards include topics like investigations into the retail and distributive services sector, merchandising and display, and sales and finance. Remember that if you are doing some units from another GNVQ, like Business, you can also use the opportunities from that GNVQ.

Topic area 1
Buying, selling, sales and finance

Planning and interpreting information
There should be opportunities to look at simple profit and loss statements, interpreting what the information means for the business. You may have to show you can use documents like these to demonstrate that you know the difference between income and profit. Purchase orders, invoices and statements of accounts are other documents that contain numbers.

You might be able to get hold of company documentation like an annual report that provides numerical information on overhead costs, investing in stock, stakeholder payments and dealing with relevant taxes. There will be a host of other numerical information too. This would be a good opportunity to show that you can work with relevant retail and distributive services information as well as a chance to generate evidence for your Application of Number. While you try to interpret the different types of numerical information, take note of how the company has presented it. You will be able to judge for yourself whether or not you think their methods are effective. You may also get some ideas for presenting your own information.

Computer-based electronic systems are also used to record, store and retrieve sales and financial data. If you have the chance, use some print-outs from these systems; they may be good sources of numerical information. This might be an opportunity to work with a large set of data with at least 20 items, to work out different averages (mean, mode and median), and to use ranges that describe the spread.

Calculating

There will be opportunities for using financial information in several different ways to measure sales, to measure profits and to forecast cash flows. Explaining the different uses for money derived from sales (overheads, investments, stakeholder payments, taxation, savings, etc.) and presenting your findings as a pie chart will mean having to do some calculations and conversions.

Interpreting results and presenting findings

There will be several different types of information that you could present graphically. One obvious example is a company's share performance over a certain period of time presented as a graph. Very often financial pages in newspapers will have examples to look at for help. Without getting too bogged down in all the complex jargon, just concentrate on how the newspaper presents the graph, the scales they use, the labelling and the titles. The different costs in the selling price can be explained quite effectively using a pie chart.

Topic area 2
Merchandising and display

Planning and interpreting information

When you are looking at how outlets measure the effectiveness of their display and merchandising activities, you may have to:

- Look at figures relating to the performance of displayed merchandise and figures relating to changes in sales of displayed items.
- Understand the physical dimensions and space of the outlets by interpreting plans that show the floor area and/or the amount of available display space or shelf space.

Calculating

Looking at space will lead to exploring space measurements and the related costs. Space measurements and floor plans could involve straightforward scales and working out areas of rectangular shapes (e.g. floor areas) or even working out volumes of rectangular-based spaces (e.g. display cabinets or cases). These would be good level 1 activities. At level 2 you would be expected to show that you could work out dimensions

from scale drawings (e.g. using a 1:20 scale) and that you could work out more complex areas and volumes. For example, the area of L-shaped floor spaces, or the number of units of a product that would be needed to fill a given space (e.g. how many special-offer tins of beans would fit into a display cabinet).

By looking at how effective an existing company's display and merchandising is, you will be able to generate lots of numerical information. You could do this by making accurate observations of how many customers in a certain time period notice or select certain display items and the numbers who either fail to notice them or who notice them but don't buy them. You could use the tally method described in Part 1 to log the reactions of different customers. This type of survey could involve working with a large set of data (at level 2 you to have to deal with a set of data containing a minimum of 20 items). You could look at averages in your data. It could also involve conversions between fractions, decimals and percentages.

Interpreting results and presenting findings

One method of presenting information might be to use pictograms as an interesting and effective graphical way to present your findings.

You might think of working out the different proportions of display space taken up by the selected display products and show this as a pie chart.

You may want to create your own plans and use you own scale to show how an area could be laid out. By using an existing space in an outlet, you could come up with an alternative layout and display. This would involve:

* Taking measurements accurately
* Making appropriate plans for a display

If you decide to do a customer survey to show the effectiveness of some display or merchandising, you will have several options for presenting your findings graphically.

Topic area 3
Investigating the retail and distributive services sector

Planning and interpreting information

If you are going to research the contribution the sector makes to the local and/or national economy, you may have to interpret government statistics or statistics based on your area. Very often this type of information comes in tables or in graphs and charts.

Doing simple comparisons of locations of different outlets could involve using maps and working out distances from residential areas, main communications links, or working out car parking spaces or areas. This would involve working with scales and working out sizes or distances from maps and being able to comment on the degree of accuracy.

Calculating

Straightforward activities could be a simple survey of the types of outlet in your area, counting the different numbers of independent and multiple retail shops, superstores and hypermarkets, specialist shops, department stores, catalogue stores, convenience stores and discounters. Slightly more complex might be a closer look at one category like specialist shops, recording what services they provide or the types of product they sell. This type of work should allow you to work with straightforward calculations like using simple fractions and percentages.

If you were comparing different supermarkets or hypermarkets, you could look at information to do with floor space or car parking, or you could carry out a survey of the price of the same products in each store. This will involve using a number of different calculations after you have collected the data.

At a more complex level, you could be looking at the contribution that retail and/or distribution makes to the local and national economy in terms of the numbers of people employed or the amounts of money created. You could look at different trends over a number of years. It will really depend on the quality and amount of information you can get hold of.

Interpreting results and presenting findings

All the previous suggestions will create opportunities to present your work using different graphical methods. You will also have an opportunity to select methods that are more effective and more appropriate than others. Some of the suggestions will allow you to create graphs that show trends you may have found, or to show comparisons between different store prices using charts.

Further opportunities for evidence

Looking after money

Bank and credit card statements are sources of information that involve numbers. They also show a range of calculations that take place. This is not just adding (with credits made as money is put into an account) and subtraction as money is taken out (debited) or as charges are made. Credit statements also involve a calculation when interest charges are made. You could work out what percentage interest charge is being applied.

One number exercise that contributes to a better understanding of banking is to take a range of bank accounts and compare their interest rates. You could do this by looking at what would happen to the same amount of money if it were put in each account and saved there for a year. You need to work out how much interest it would make in the different accounts.

Delivery services

There will be direct opportunities to produce evidence when looking at costs involved in delivery. You might need to:

- Calculate costs directly charged to customers in addition to the product price, expressing the additional costs as an percentage.

What you must know
Part 1: The Learning Curve will help you with the knowledge you need.

What you must do
Part 2: The Bottom Line will help you with the evidence you need.

- Show the contribution that delivery costs make to the total price of a product, where the cost of delivery is already included in the price.

There are also simple opportunities in working out the volume of different lorries and vans, perhaps even working out how much of a certain product they could then transport. By using the same product for different sized vans and lorries, you will be able to present some interesting comparative data.

Science GNVQ

PART ONE • FOUNDATION • INTERMEDIATE

About the specifications
The Science awards include the study of topics like applying practical skills in science, experimenting and carrying out scientific work and applying scientific knowledge, skills and understanding.

See also: **Science GCSE**, page 78

Topic area 1
Measuring, observing and applying practical skills in science

Planning and interpreting information
Making observations and measurements involves practical skills used in many GNVQ units. You will need to be able to set up instruments and take down results from their scales and from other kinds of read-out. Here are some common quantities and the units they might be measured in:

- **Mass:** kilogram (kg), gram (g)
- **Length:** kilometre (km), metre (m), centimetre (cm), millimetre (mm)
- **Volume:** cubic metre (m^3), cubic centimetre (cm^3), cubic decimetre (dm^3), millilitre (ml)
- **Time:** hour (h), minute (min), second (s)
- **Temperature:** degree Celsius (°C)
- **Voltage:** volt (V); voltage is sometimes called potential difference
- **Current:** ampere (A)
- **Resistance:** ohm (Ω)
- **Force:** newton (N)

Besides using instruments, you will obtain these quantities by reading tables, charts, diagrams or line graphs (at level 1) and you must show that you can use and interpret a graph (at level 2).

Remember you should keep evidence that shows you were able to select appropriate instruments to help you get the results you needed. You also need to be clear about your purpose and what you are trying to do.

Calculating

In scientific work it is common to use a formula to get new information from measurements that you have made. For example, you could be calculating resistance using measurements for voltage and current then using the formula $R = V/I$ to calculate the resistance. This would be a useful level 2 example.

After reading values from instruments or from tables, you may need to convert from one unit to another, perhaps from cubic metres to litres. Level 1 requires more straightforward calculations to establish average values and to work out volumes. You may also need to work with proportions and amounts when experimenting.

Interpreting results and presenting findings

You can write up the results in your laboratory notebooks using appropriate ways of presenting your findings. Make appropriate use of charts, graphs and diagrams. You will need to have evidence for a range of activities and experiments in your laboratory notebook, so you should have a good opportunity to present numerical information in various ways.

Topic area 2
Scientific work

Planning and interpreting information

There will be an opportunity to use secondary sources of numerical information. For manufacturing materials, density, melting and boiling points, etc., are likely to be presented in tables. Doing work with living organisms may involve taking measurements and making estimates with varying degrees of accuracy.

Calculating

You will also have opportunities to measure and calculate properties of materials like density, brittleness, hardness, stiffness, tensile strength, electrical resistance and thermal conductivity. There might also be opportunities to compare properties that will involve using formulas and handling statistics. Dealing with the results of your practical work will also mean using amounts and sizes, scales and proportions, formulas and equations.

Interpreting results and presenting findings

When producing reports to show your findings and any conclusions that you draw, you will have the opportunity to present your findings in appropriate ways. Where appropriate, try to use graphs, charts and diagrams to help explain or illustrate your findings.

Topic area 3
Scientific knowledge, understanding and skills

Planning and interpreting information

Typical opportunities with electrical and electronic devices:

- Interpreting settings of monitoring and control devices such as thermostats.
- Interpreting the results from more straightforward equipment like thermometers.

Typical opportunities with mechanical machines:

- Measuring input and output forces.
- Calculating the work done.

Typical opportunities with living organisms:

- Monitoring activity and conditions such as reading temperatures.

Calculating

Typical calculations with chemical equations:

- Calculating the mass of a product.
- Calculating the percentage yields of reactions.
- Calculating the costs for different quantities of product.

Typical calculations with mechanical machines:

- Calculating the work done.

Interpreting results and presenting findings

The units ask you to explain the principles and workings of various scientific devices and processes. Good use of diagrams, graphs and charts will help you gain good grades in the units as well as showing your key skills.

Further opportunities for evidence

Growing plants

Topics like these will involve monitoring growth, perhaps using thermometers to measure temperature; there could be opportunities for measuring out volumes of liquid, measuring the mass of solids, or even measuring the height of plants. Other number opportunities could involve working out costs and working out what price to charge. This provides opportunities for interpreting numbers and using them in calculations.

Working with food

There will be opportunities to measure quantities of food, work with different cooking times, and convert cooking temperatures from electric to gas. Working more closely with food will give you opportunities to work with calories and energy values. You could even begin to look at the different percentages (%) involved in the typical values of food that can be found on the food packaging. Just look at the numbers on a tin of beans or a packet of cereal; think about the calculations they involve.

Health and fitness

There will be opportunities to measure pulse rates before and after exercise using a timer. Other opportunities for working with number will be present when investigating the effects of exercise on the body. There will also be opportunities to measure out volumes of liquid or to measure out masses of food and drink. When investigating energy provided in food, you will have the opportunity to look at energy as measured in kilojoules per 100 grams of food, and also to analyse the typical energy values of protein, fibre etc. This information often appears on food packaging.

Units involving physics, chemistry and biology

- **Physics**: collecting and interpreting data from instruments, such as electrical and mechanical meters.
- **Physics**: using formulas to calculate results, such as energy and efficiency.
- **Chemistry**: calculating inputs and outputs for chemical reactions.
- **Biology**: collecting data from monitoring instruments, printed documents and electronic sources.
- **Biology**: calculating statistical data; calculating growth rates; calculating costs and prices.

What you must know
Part 1: The Learning Curve will help you with the knowledge you need.

What you must do
Part 2: The Bottom Line will help you with the evidence you need.

Opportunities

Evidence from everyday sources

When you are confident with numbers, you will not even realise that you are using them. Numbers become so much a part of finding out, making clear and doing the job, they just seem to occur naturally. This chapter is dedicated to showing you how numbers and your use of them are already a part of your everyday life. It will also help you to generate number evidence from situations not related to qualifications.

Using information

This section uses everyday information to show how you:

- Use information and data already.
- Can use information and data more effectively.
- Could find out more from the information and data you have.
- Can present information and data to help others understand what you mean.

Practising your number skills

Each example has real text containing information or data which is simplified to show you how it is really number in action. In this section numbered lists identify what you should know, understand or do and they link these three skills with the information shown in the real text.

Personal tasks and topics

This shows how you can take the experience you have gained from the topic and prepare and plan your own investigations to produce authentic and valid evidence for your Application of Number portfolio.

The topics

The ten topics are intended to provide examples of where you can find numbers if you begin to look for them. They are not the only places you will use numbers on a daily basis. Find examples of your own and see how much you take for granted the skills you have and how much you can develop these skills and understand more about the power and influence numbers have on your everyday life.

Reading the weather

The weather update above is taken from a local newspaper. You can also find weather updates like this in national newspapers, on teletext and on the internet. This type of information is a rich source of written and graphical material which you can interpret, use for calculations and present using your own graphs, charts and diagrams.

Using information

The two sections of this update show you the local temperatures on a diagram and the national temperatures in tables. The information is intended to show you what happened yesterday, what is expected to happen today and what is likely to happen tomorrow. All temperatures are shown in degrees Celsius (°C) and the weather is represented using symbols.

Please check that you can read and understand both diagrams (maps) and both tables. According to South-East Today, can you see that London should be sunny with a temperature of 23 °C?

Practising and using your number skills

Look at the key below to see if you can read, understand and use the information to develop your number skills.

1. These are tables which are sources of relevant information.
2. These are diagrams (maps) which are sources of relevant information.
3. These are numbers that are used to show temperatures in °C and symbols to show what the weather is like.
4. Use the numbers in the South-East Today diagram to calculate the mean temperature.
5. Use the numbers in the South-East Tomorrow diagram to calculate the mean temperature. Which day has the higher mean temperature?
   Use the numbers in the Britain Today table to calculate the mean national temperature. What can you say about the national mean and the South-East mean for today?
5. Look at the readings for temperatures in the Around Britain Yesterday table and calculate the mean, median and mode.
6. Use the formula for converting Celsius to Fahrenheit ($F = \frac{9}{5}C + 32$) and practice converting the temperatures shown in the diagrams and tables.
7. Use the set of data in the Britain Today table to draw a bar graph to compare the temperatures from the ten different areas of Britain.
8. Use the set of data in the Around Britain Yesterday table to construct a frequency table (fair, cloudy, sunny) and show your results using a chart and a graph (e.g. bar graph and pie chart).

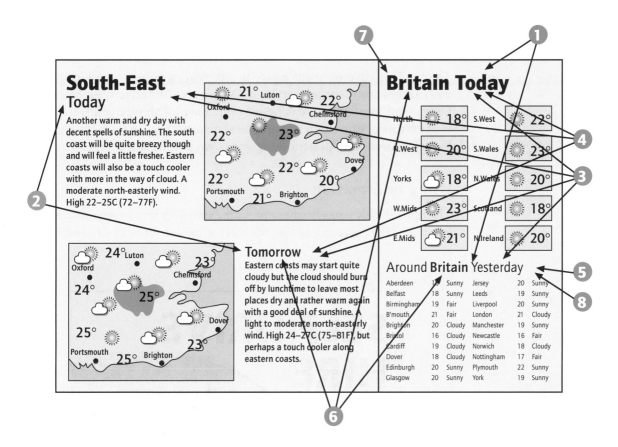

South-East
Today

Another warm and dry day with decent spells of sunshine. The south coast will be quite breezy though and will feel a little fresher. Eastern coasts will also be a touch cooler with more in the way of cloud. A moderate north-easterly wind. High 22–25C (72–77F).

Tomorrow

Eastern coasts may start quite cloudy but the cloud should burn off by lunchtime to leave most places dry and rather warm again with a good deal of sunshine. A light to moderate north-easterly wind. High 24–27C (75–81F), but perhaps a touch cooler along eastern coasts.

Britain Today

North	18°	S.West	22°
N.West	20°	S.Wales	23°
Yorks	18°	N.Wales	20°
W.Mids	23°	Scotland	18°
E.Mids	21°	N.Ireland	20°

Around **Britain** Yesterday

Aberdeen	13	Sunny	Jersey	20	Sunny
Belfast	18	Sunny	Leeds	19	Sunny
Birmingham	19	Fair	Liverpool	20	Sunny
B'mouth	21	Fair	London	21	Cloudy
Brighton	20	Cloudy	Manchester	19	Sunny
Bristol	16	Cloudy	Newcastle	16	Fair
Cardiff	19	Cloudy	Norwich	18	Cloudy
Dover	18	Cloudy	Nottingham	17	Fair
Edinburgh	20	Sunny	Plymouth	22	Sunny
Glasgow	20	Sunny	York	19	Sunny

Personal tasks and topics

This type of topic will provide you with opportunities to develop and apply your number skills as you find out information which is helpful to you at home and when you are planning your leisure time. When you are investigating this sort of information it will involve you in interpreting, calculating and explaining your findings using data and formulas.

The knowledge, skills and understanding you have practised here can be used again to generate evidence for the substantial activity where you need to provide evidence: interpreting information, carrying out calculations, interpreting results and presenting your findings.

The data (interpreting information and carrying out calculations) you need can come from your own measurements (e.g. temperature or rainfall) or it could come from written or graphical material (e.g. newspapers or teletext) which you have collected over an extended period of time (e.g. each day for a month).

The range of calculations you will use will depend upon what you are reporting or investigating, but in this area they are likely to include handling statistics and using formulas. The interpretation and presentation of your findings should use at least one graph and one chart.

Hiring a car

The car hire advertisement above is a typical example of how companies and garages promote their services. You can also find advertisements for car hire in your local press and in holiday brochures. This type of advertisement is a rich source of written and graphical material that you can interpret, use for calculations and present using your own graphs and charts.

Using information

The table in this advertisement provides you with the charges for car hire. It sets out the costs of car hire for three different types of car and for dif-

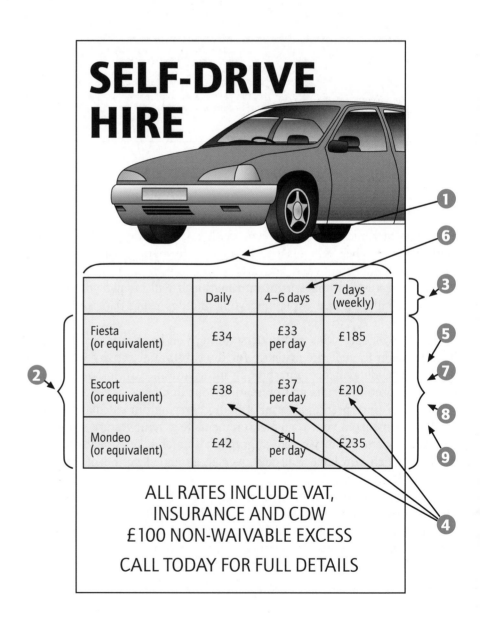

ferent lengths of time. The table is set out in a way that helps you compare costs of the different cars for the different number of days. All costs are in pounds (£) and the minimum rate is for one day.

Please check that you can read and understand the table. Do you understand the meaning of the words 'daily' and 'weekly' and the abbreviations VAT and CDW?

Practising and using your number skills

Look at the key below to see if you can read, understand and use the information to develop your number skills.

1. The table is a source of relevant information using graphical material.
2. These are the different categories or types of car available for hire.
3. These are the different bands of charges for the different categories or types of car.
4. These are the different costs for each car in pounds (£).
5. Use the table to find out the average (mean) cost of hiring each type of car for one day. What can you say about each cost when compared with the given daily rate? Why is this? Write each of your answers accurately to (a) the nearest penny, (b) the nearest 10p, (c) the nearest pound. Which would be the most sensible amount to work with? Why?
6. Use the table and the information it contains to produce a more detailed table that has a separate column showing the charge for each car for between 1 and 7 days. Use the cost bands from the original table. What do you notice about the 6-day charge for each type of car?
7. Use the information in the table to construct a series of charts or graphs to compare the costs and charges for each type of car over a 7-day period Show how these charts or tables can be used to help you decide on the best value for money.
8. Collect information on car hire from other sources and represent the costs and charges graphically so they can be compared with the information on this advertisement.
9. When you operate as a business you can sometimes reclaim VAT from the Inland Revenue. The charges in the original table include VAT Rewrite the table with the VAT deducted. Show your calculations clearly and give your answers to an appropriate level of accuracy.

Personal tasks and topics

This type of topic will provide you with opportunities to develop and apply your number skills as you find out information that helps you prepare for everyday activities. Reading and understanding this sort of information will involve you in interpreting, calculating and presenting your findings using numerical data.

The knowledge, skills and understanding you have developed and practised here can be used again to generate evidence for the substantial activity needed to provide evidence for the straightforward Application of Number tasks at levels 1 and 2.

The data you need can be taken from a range of sources of hiring charges from different companies. It need not be for hiring cars; it could come from hiring equipment such as sanders, tools for removing paint and wallpaper, or other DIY equipment; or it could be for renting holiday accommodation.

The range of calculations will depend upon what you are comparing but they will usually involve amounts, sizes and proportions as you work out comparable costs and periods of hire to identify the best value for money and length of use.

Discussing and explaining what you have found out is likely to involve you in using the original graphical material from which you have drawn the information. You will also need to use your own calculations and methods of identifying the most relevant and appropriate outcome in order to explain your decisions on hiring equipment, cars or accommodation.

The fun run

The map below is for a half-marathon. It is the type of simplified diagram that you will find in entry leaflets and newspapers showing the routes that races or parades are going to follow. This information is important to you

as either a runner or spectator. This type of map is a rich source of graphical material from which you can obtain relevant information, interpret it, use it for calculations and represent it in a different way, depending on the purpose of your activity.

Using information

The map is a simplified diagram that gives you:

- The route the run takes
- The direction in which the runners go
- The distances in miles
- A key for the location of facilities

The map or diagram is set out to help runners plan their race and spectators to decide where they want to watch.

Please check that you can read and understand the diagram. Do you know how long the run is and why it is called a half-marathon?

Practising and using your number skills

Check at the key points below to see if you can read, understand and use the information to develop your number skills.

- The diagram is a source of relevant information using graphical material.
- These are the distances in miles.
- This is the key that shows you where the facilities are to be found on the route.
- The arrows show the direction the runners take.
- Use the diagram to find out the position of the mile markers, toilets, medical stations and refreshment stations. Arrange this information in a table to help a runner plan where to take on more liquid.
- Is the diagram drawn to scale? Use the information in the diagram to check your answer. You will need a ruler to help you.
- Runners often help themselves to get through a long race by setting targets: I'm now three-quarters of the way round – only another quarter to go!. Break this run down into four parts and draw a table to show the link between street names (and other features) and each of the four stages (or quarters) of the race. You will need to draw up a list starting with Saltmarket and ending with the People's Palace.
- Distances along the route are given in miles but most races are now measured in kilometres. Draw a table to show the distances in both miles and kilometres. Then use the information on your conversion table to construct a straight line on a graph which converts miles to kilometres for 0–26 miles, the distance for a full marathon.

Personal tasks and topics

This type of topic will provide you with opportunities to develop and

apply your number skills through participating in sporting activities, as a participant, spectator or organiser.

The knowledge, skills and understanding you have developed and practised can be used again to generate evidence for the substantial activity needed to provide evidence for the straightforward tasks at level 2 or for individual tasks at level 1.

You could use races or routes for a range of activities such as races including Formula One grand prix or travel plans for holidays. The greater your involvement in planning, preparing, researching, recording and providing information, the more likely you are to meet the full requirements of level 2.

Managing money

The document below is a typical weekly payslip. If you have a part-time or full-time job your payslip may look different from this but the information it gives is standard. A payslip is a rich source of numerical information and provides you with an opportunity to interpret numbers and use them for calculations. If you are opening a bank account or seeking a loan, you will also be expected to show how the information included on your payslip supports your application. This is an important part of interpreting and presenting.

Using information

The payslip is laid out simply to enable you to see quickly what you have earned, what deductions (off-takes) have been made to your earnings and, most importantly, what your take-home pay is. A payslip will also usually act as a record of your earnings so far during the tax year, as well as showing you what you have paid in tax, National Insurance or pension. All

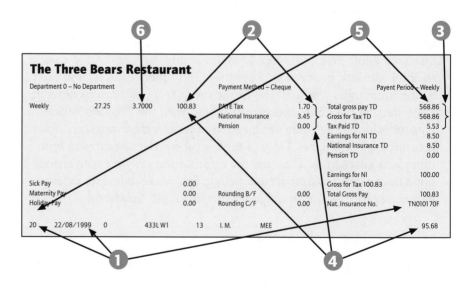

amounts are in pounds sterling and to two decimal places. A payslip like this is a good example of reading and understanding numbers used in different ways. This is because as well as having numbers use for amounts of money, you have numbers used for reference. Two examples of a reference number are the date and the National Insurance number. Numbers are also used for counting to show which tax week the payslip is for.

Practising and using your number skills

Look at the key below to see if you can read, understand and use the information to develop your number skills.

1. This shows you numbers used for reference – the week number within the tax year, the date and the National Insurance number.
2. This is what you have earned and what deductions have been made to your earnings.
3. This is what you have earned and paid in contributions to tax, National Insurance and pension since the start of the tax year.
4. Using the information on the payslip, show how your employer calculated what your take-home pay was. What percentage of your pay was deducted for this week? Using a similar method, can you show what your total **net** pay (total take-home pay) has been since the start of the tax year?
5. Using the **gross** pay given by your employer so far this year, calculate your mean weekly gross pay then round it up to the nearest penny. The difference between the current weekly rate and the mean weekly rate is that you are working more during your holidays. Calculate how much you would have earned this year so far if you had been working for as long and with the same rate of pay as this week. Show all your calculations and round to the nearest penny.
6. Your payslip shows you your hourly rate. Use it to construct a graph to show your possible earnings for a normal forty-hour week. This will help you quickly check how much you will earn at the end of any week once you know how many hours you have worked.

Personal tasks and topics

Information that deals with managing money provides you with opportunities to select and apply your number skills in a very real and relevant way. Everyone has to manage money or have their money managed for them by others. The sources for this are many and include:

- Payslips (like the one opposite).
- Monthly bank statements.
- Savings accounts from building societies.
- Receipts from cash machines (ATMs).
- Credit card accounts.

All are rich sources of interpreting, calculating and selecting information. If a particular project is planned, perhaps budgeting for a holiday, buying

a car or renting a flat, the accounts that monitor, record and represent your income and expenditure will provide you with valid and detailed evidence for Application of Number at levels 1 and 2.

Recipes

The chart below shows the roasting times for meat and poultry. It is typical of the charts or tables that you find in recipe books or the manuals provided with cookers or microwave ovens. There are several reasons why this chart is so useful:

- It has a variety of different types of numerical information.
- It uses a graphical form.
- It uses numbers for different types of measurements.
- It compares measurements for different systems such as kilogrammes (kg) and pounds (lb).

Using information

The chart or table is laid out simply to show different types of meat, the different temperature settings in degrees Celsius (°C) and the cooking times. A chart like this contains all the variables necessary to calculate the

Roasting Chart

Meat	Conventional main oven temperature (°C)	Second fan oven temperature (°C)	Cooking time (t)
Beef (B)	190–200	180–190	20–35 minutes per$\frac{1}{2}$kg (1 lb) and 20–35 minutes over
Mutton and lamb (M)	190–200	180–190	25–35 minutes per$\frac{1}{2}$kg (1 lb) and 25–35 minutes over
Pork and veal (P)	190–200	180–190	30–40 minutes per$\frac{1}{2}$kg (1 lb) and 30–40 minutes over
Ham (H)	190–200	180–190	30–40 minutes per$\frac{1}{2}$kg (1 lb) and 30–40 minutes over
Chicken (C)	190–200	180–190	15–20 minutes per$\frac{1}{2}$kg (1 lb) and 20 minutes over
Turkey and Goose (T)	190–200	180–190	15–20 minutes per$\frac{1}{2}$kg (1 lb) up to $3\frac{1}{2}$ kg (7 lb) then 10 minutes per$\frac{1}{2}$kg (1 lb)
Duck (D)	190–200	180–190	25–35 minutes per$\frac{1}{2}$kg (1 lb) and 25–35 minutes over
Pheasant (Ph)	190–200	180–190	35–40 minutes per$\frac{1}{2}$kg (1 lb) and 35–40 minutes over

cooking times for joints of meat and poultry of any size. Meat is not the only component of a meal, but by using similar charts for the other items you could plan and prepare a whole dinner party. Besides that, these charts show you how simple numerical information can be manipulated to provide quite complex data. Charts and recipes like this provide good opportunities for interpreting information, calculating amounts and sizes, using formulas and, in certain circumstances, presenting your findings to others.

Please check that you can read and understand the chart. For instance, do you know what type of oven you will be using and whether your meat or poultry will be weighed in kilograms (kg) or pounds (lb)? This topic assumes you know the difference between pork and beef (meat), chicken and duck (poultry)!

Practising and using your number skills

Look at the key below to see if you can use the chart to read, understand and use the information to develop your number skills.

1. This shows you the temperatures that each type of oven should be set at for cooking. Have you any idea why fan ovens are consistently 10 °C lower?
2. This shows you the cooking time for different weights of meat. Notice the approximation which gives $\frac{1}{2}$ kg as equivalent to 1 lb.
3. Using the information in the table and the formula for converting °C into °F ($F = \frac{9}{5}C + 32$), rewrite the different cooking temperatures for beef.
4. The cooking times given can be rewritten into simple formulas that will help you work out the actual cooking time for any weight of meat or poultry. Draw up a simple table for meat and cooking time. Use the given letter for the weights of the meat and t for time, to create a formula for each type of meat. Plot your graph in hours and use the mean of the times given (e.g. mean of 30–44 = 35 minutes)
5. Formulas like the ones you have developed above can be used to show the cooking times for different weights of the same meat. Use the information in your chart and the formulas in your table to draw a graph for joints of lamb up to 4 kg. Mark with a cross the cooking times for a joint of 2.5 kg and a joint of 4 lb.
6. In points 4 and 5 you have used the mean of the times for weight per $\frac{1}{2}$ kg. The times such as 25–35 minutes per $\frac{1}{2}$ kg or the temperatures such as 190–200 °C describe the range. For one of the meats, draw axes for time in minutes and weight in kilograms. Draw a graph for each whole-minute cooking time of the range, i.e. if the range is 25–30 minutes you will need to use six different graphs (25, 26, 27, 28, 29 and 30 minutes). What do you notice about the lines for each graph? What is the range for cooking a piece of meat that weighs 3 kg?

Personal tasks and topics

Activities like those described above will provide you with the Application of Number evidence towards levels 1 and 2. Other opportunities to plan and complete the substantial activity, including tasks that will also provide evidence of interpreting and presenting, could be offered when:

- Planning and budgeting for a party.
- Organising and scheduling preparation and cooking times for an event.
- Catering for a function.

Although the information here has used a conversion chart for cooking times, charts like this are used extensively in DIY activities. They are usually found in information leaflets, on the sides of packages or tins, or in instruction manuals.

Booking a holiday

The table opposite is taken from a holiday brochure. This type of table is commonly used by travel agents to provide you with all the information you need to work out the cost of a holiday. As the numbers and ages vary within groups of holidaymakers, the table has to provide a range of information to include these variables.

A table like this is a complex mixture of numbers, used for:

- Classification, such as ages or number of nights
- Reference, such as dates
- Costs of different group size

Using information

The table is laid out to show three different sites:

- Costa C53A02
- Los Amigos C53A03
- Las Vegas C53A04

It also provides you with all the different combinations of group size and holiday dates. Before using a table like this you will have to have a range of other relevant information including:

- When you want to take your holiday
- How many there will be in your party
- What type of accommodation you want
- The ages of any children in your party
- How much you can afford

HOLIDAYS IN LANZAROTE

Departures on or between	COSTA C53A02 SELF CATERING								LOS AMIGOS C53A03 SELF CATERING						LAS VEGAS C53A04 SELF CATERING							
Room Type	1 Bedroom Apartment				Studio		Children 2–16 Years		1 Bedroom Apartment				Children 2–16 Years		1 Bedroom Apartment						Children 2–16 Years	
No. Adults Sharing	3		2		2		1st	2nd	3		2		1st	2nd	4		3		2		1st	2nd
Number of Nights	7	14	7	14	7	14	7/14	7/14	7	14	7	14	7/14	7/14	7	14	7	14	7	14	7/14	7/14
01 Apr–12 Apr	239	335	269	395	255	349	99	99	249	299	279	355	129	129	245	245	255	265	275	299	89	89
13 Apr–19 Apr	239	389	269	505	255	405	169	169	249	379	369	505	199	195	245	409	375	435	255	469	185	185
20 Apr–24 Apr	299	389	355	505	315	405	169	169	359	409	409	505	199	199	355	375	375	409	409	469	185	185
25 Apr–30 Apr	239	335	269	395	255	349	99	99	249	299	279	355	129	129	245	245	255	265	275	299	89	89
01 May–17 May	265	305	305	385	275	315	99	149	249	279	279	349	99	99	259	279	285	325	319	389	99	149
18 May–24 May	275	385	315	435	285	395	119	149	259	289	289	399	129	129	259	379	285	409	319	469	129	149
25 May–29 May	399	435	445	509	409	425	179	199	379	409	415	479	179	179	385	385	405	425	439	495	179	199
30 May–14 Jun	305	355	355	435	325	375	129	209	289	329	319	359	99	99	315	325	329	345	359	435	129	209
15 Jun–21 Jun	329	375	379	455	345	405	129	219	315	355	349	419	99	99	329	339	335	375	375	465	129	219
22 Jun–05 Jul	345	389	385	469	365	439	129	229	335	389	369	455	129	129	339	375	355	415	395	495	139	229
06 Jul–12 Jul	345	389	385	469	369	445	129	229	335	389	369	455	129	129	345	379	359	419	399	499	179	229
13 Jul–19 Jul	395	475	435	565	419	519	179	239	389	459	419	549	149	149	389	445	415	495	455	585	179	239

(Left margin label: DEPARTURES ON OR BETWEEN. Accom. Name / Accom. Code / Board Basis are listed at the head of the table.)

Amenities
- Freshwater swimming pool
- Poolside sun terrace with loungers
- Reception (open 9.00 am to 4 pm Mon–Sat)
- 400 metres from resort centre bars and restaurants
- 500 metres from sandy beach
- Low-rise, two storey complex
- Mini-market 75 metres

Accommodation
Bright well-furnished one-bedroom apartments have kitchenette with fridge, oven and cooking rings, bathroom and balcony or terrace. Maid service five times a week and weekly linen change.

Please check that you can read and understand the table. Can you see how numbers are used for different purposes? The pound sign (£) is not found anywhere in this table although all costs are in pounds.

Practising and using your number skills

Look at the key below to see if you can use the table to read, understand and use the information to develop your number skills.

1. This gives you the different categories of information, including accommodation, references for booking and dates for holidays.
2. This gives you the information for the three different sites. Can you see where each begins and ends?
3. This is the banded cost for each type of apartment for each number of people for each holiday week. You read this information across the page.
4. Using the table, can you see how much it would cost for you and a friend, at £435 each, to stay in a one-bedroom apartment at Costa for a 7-night holiday beginning 13 July?
5. Children are classified as being between the ages of 2 and 16 years. If you added a 15-year-old friend to the holiday, can you work out what the new overall cost would be?

6. Sometimes we decide on a holiday based on the budget we have. This means you have a fixed amount of money to spend and then look for something that falls within your budget. Looking for holidays this way means you have to be more flexible about where you stay, when you go and how long you go for. Look at the entries for the week beginning 1 May. In Las Vegas apartments, 14 nights are only slightly more expensive than 7 nights in the same accommodation during the week beginning 6 July. Set yourself a budget for accommodation of, say, £390 each; see what you can find for your holiday and arrange this information so it can be clearly understood by others.

Personal tasks and topics

Tables and charts that present relevant information, both written and graphical, provide you with opportunities to select, read, understand, interpret, calculate and represent numerical information. This may be done quickly and simply like these examples. However, they may also provide the basis for much more extensive research from a range of sources such as other brochures, teletext, and face-to-face discussions with travel agents.

The extent to which you follow up this topic will depend upon the level and relevance of evidence for your Application of Number portfolio. The following suggestions could, if researched, combined and presented effectively, meet the requirements of level 2 but would certainly provide you with evidence for individual tasks at levels 1 and 2. These activities include:

- Comparing and contrasting information from a range of holiday companies in written, graphical and electronic sources using a specified budget.
- Planning, preparing costs for, and presenting findings to a group on potential holiday arrangements.
- Planning your own holiday, including accommodation, currency and travel arrangements.

Crossing the channel

The map of the English Channel below shows the main ports in England and France and the main routes between them. It has been simplified by removing detailed information but it is still intended to be accurate in terms of distance. You can tell this because the map has a scale beside it. This type of source is called graphical material in key skills; it is a secondary source because you will be using someone else's information rather than finding your own from observation.

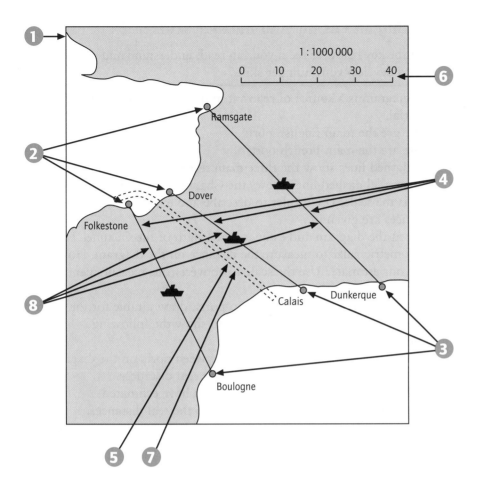

Using information

Maps like this are variously described as charts, diagrams, drawings or plans. For Application of Number purposes, they are diagrams that give you information on:

- The location of the major ports
- The relative positions of major ports
- The major ferry routes between English and French ports
- The linear distances between ports
- The position of the Channel Tunnel
- A scale to calculate distances

A small-scale map like this will not provide distances that are totally precise; it is normally used to help you decide on ferry terminals and destinations so that you can work out routes, times and approximate distances.

Please check that you can read and understand the diagram. Do you know which part of the country it shows and can you find it on a map of the United Kingdom?

Opportunities

Practising and using your number skills

Look at the key below to see if you can read, understand and use the information to develop your number skills.

1. The diagram is a source of relevant information from graphical material.
2. These are the main English ports.
3. These are the main French ports.
4. The dashed lines show the three main ferry routes.
5. The parallel dashed lines shows the Channel Tunnel Rail Link.
6. This is the scale. Use a ruler to describe and explain what the real distances are given in.
7. Look at the diagram and estimate the length of the Channel Tunnel. Use a metric ruler to measure the distance on the diagram. How close was your estimate? Use the scale to convert your measurement to the real distance.
8. Using the scale and information on ports, draw a table for the main routes between England and France to show the following information:
   - Estimates of the actual distances between ports on the diagram.
   - Conversions of your estimates to the real distances.
   - Measured values for the distances you have estimated.
   - Conversions of your measurements to the real distances.
     How good were you at estimating?

Personal tasks and topics

This type of topic will provide you with opportunities to practice reading and understanding graphical material, using your understanding of number to approximate and estimate and using scales to convert and find sizes.

The knowledge, techniques and understanding you have developed and practised can be used again to generate evidence for either individual tasks in the application of number at levels 1 or 2 or to work on a more extended activity that includes all three tasks involving interpreting, calculating and presenting.

The extent to which you collect relevant evidence will depend upon how much you follow up this topic. Here are two suggestions that could be researched:

- Using the basic information provided along with ferry times for the various ports and the Channel Tunnel schedule and costs, work out and provide information that compares costs, times and speeds between the various ports.
- Look at other similar links between ports that are most relevant to you such as Liverpool and Ireland, Holyhead and Ireland, or Weymouth and the Channel Islands. Identify the rates, the different types of craft, such as hydrofoil and ferry, and their different times and costs. Use them to present and compare data for a clear purpose.

Joining an evening class

The extract below is from an adult education brochure that provides students with information on fees. It is an example of a source of relevant information that contains both written and graphical material. This is because although the information is presented in two tables, the majority of the information is given using written text. Numbers are hardly used

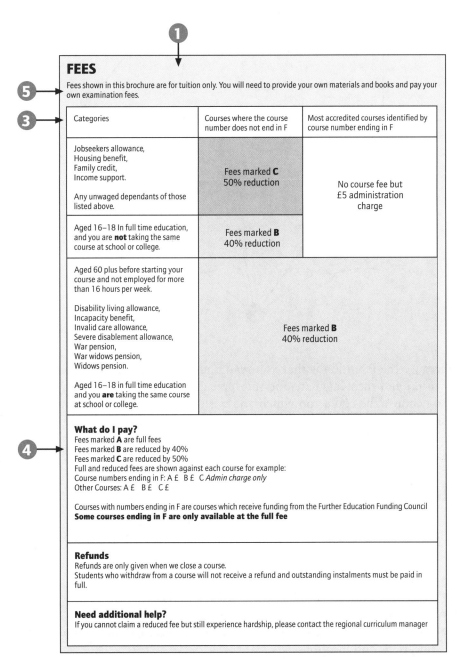

FEES

5 Fees shown in this brochure are for tuition only. You will need to provide your own materials and books and pay your own examination fees.

3 Categories	Courses where the course number does not end in F	Most accredited courses identified by course number ending in F
Jobseekers allowance, Housing benefit, Family credit, Income support. Any unwaged dependants of those listed above.	Fees marked **C** 50% reduction	No course fee but £5 administration charge
Aged 16–18 In full time education, and you **are not** taking the same course at school or college.	Fees marked **B** 40% reduction	
Aged 60 plus before starting your course and not employed for more than 16 hours per week. Disability living allowance, Incapacity benefit, Invalid care allowance, Severe disablement allowance, War pension, War widows pension, Widows pension. Aged 16–18 in full time education and you **are** taking the same course at school or college.	Fees marked **B** 40% reduction	

What do I pay?
Fees marked **A** are full fees
Fees marked **B** are reduced by 40%
Fees marked **C** are reduced by 50%
Full and reduced fees are shown against each course for example:
Course numbers ending in F: A £   B £   C *Admin charge only*
Other Courses: A £   B £   C £

Courses with numbers ending in F are courses which receive funding from the Further Education Funding Council
Some courses ending in F are only available at the full fee

Refunds
Refunds are only given when we close a course.
Students who withdraw from a course will not receive a refund and outstanding instalments must be paid in full.

Need additional help?
If you cannot claim a reduced fee but still experience hardship, please contact the regional curriculum manager

Opportunities

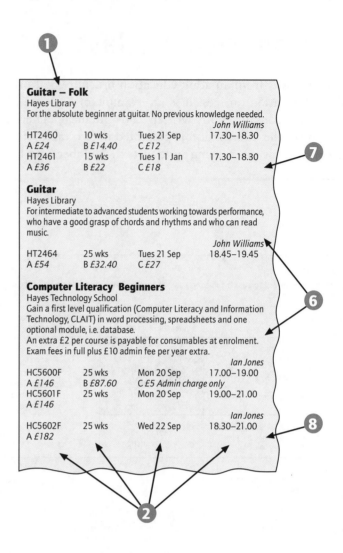

Guitar – Folk
Hayes Library
For the absolute beginner at guitar. No previous knowledge needed.
John Williams

HT2460	10 wks	Tues 21 Sep	17.30–18.30
A *£24*	B *£14.40*	C *£12*	
HT2461	15 wks	Tues 1 1 Jan	17.30–18.30
A *£36*	B *£22*	C *£18*	

Guitar
Hayes Library
For intermediate to advanced students working towards performance, who have a good grasp of chords and rhythms and who can read music.
John Williams

| HT2464 | 25 wks | Tues 21 Sep | 18.45–19.45 |
| A *£54* | B *£32.40* | C *£27* | |

Computer Literacy Beginners
Hayes Technology School
Gain a first level qualification (Computer Literacy and Information Technology, CLAIT) in word processing, spreadsheets and one optional module, i.e. database.
An extra £2 per course is payable for consumables at enrolment.
Exam fees in full plus £10 admin fee per year extra.
Ian Jones

HC5600F	25 wks	Mon 20 Sep	17.00–19.00
A *£146*	B *£87.60*	C *£5 Admin charge only*	
HC5601F	25 wks	Mon 20 Sep	19.00–21.00
A *£146*			
			Ian Jones
HC5602F	25 wks	Wed 22 Sep	18.30–21.00
A *£182*			

because the intention is that you read and understand this piece of information and then calculate and interpret elsewhere in the brochure. Then you choose the course on which you wish to enrol, obtain the course fee, find out when the course takes place and calculate how much you have to pay. An activity like this is not substantial but it does include tasks from each part of the Application of Number key skill at levels 1 and 2.

Using information

These tables and the example of a course description provide you with all the information you need to join a class. Information like this must try to cover:

- The categories of people joining classes.
- The different scales of fees they will be charged.
- The range of different classes available to them.
- Information specific to each class, such as reference code, number of meetings and location.

Practising and using your number skills

Look at the key below to see if you can read, understand and use the information to develop your number skills.

1. The table and the course descriptions are sources of relevant information from written material.

2. The course descriptions use numbers in different ways – as references, for amounts, for dates and times.

3. The categories section tries to cover the full range of different types of people who might enrol on courses and it links them to the fee bands.

4. There are four types of fee band. The first three are easy to spot but can you find the fourth?

5. Joining a course will cost you more than just the enrolment fee. Read the information and make a list of other potential costs.

6. Look at the course descriptions for guitar lessons and computer literacy lessons. Can you work out these items:
   - How long each of the classes is.
   - What the hourly rate is for each category for each class (to the penny).
   - Which fee you would pay.

7. If you joined a folk guitar course in September and went to one lesson per week, what is the maximum number of lessons available to you during the year? How much do you think the course would cost? When would you have to pay the amounts and when would you have your last lesson? To work this out properly, you will have to decide on your student category and your fee band.

8. Try to find out from your school or college what an examination fee for CLAIT costs and use this information to calculate what the full cost of the computer literacy course would be if you joined the Wednesday class.

Personal tasks and topics

This type of topic will help you to use written information to obtain the results you need. In this case it's the right course, at the right time and for the right fee. You will need to be able to interpret numbers as they are used in a variety of different ways to provide information.

The number skills you will use here will provide you with an opportunity for evidence of straightforward tasks, especially evidence for interpreting information, interpreting results and presenting your findings, as you use your understanding of the information to choose a course and enrol on it using the correct amounts for fees.

Other tables which have more steps or stages, such as hire purchase agreements or looking at rates of interest when borrowing money from a building society, are likely to provide you with more opportunities to use multi-step calculations. This may provide you with evidence for the substantial activity required by Application of Number at level 2.

Paying for a mobile phone

The bill below is for using a mobile phone; it is typical of the sort of bill companies send you to tell you what you owe them. This type of information is different from advertising material. Advertisements provide you with different types of numerical information designed to help you choose what to buy and what schemes to join. A bill should:

- Provide clear information
- Calculate accurately
- Present instructions
- Make clear what you should do

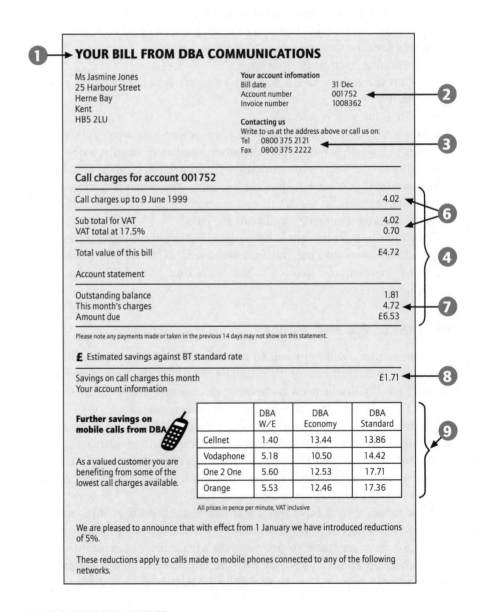

YOUR BILL FROM DBA COMMUNICATIONS

Ms Jasmine Jones
25 Harbour Street
Herne Bay
Kent
HB5 2LU

Your account infomation
Bill date   31 Dec
Account number   001752
Invoice number   1008362

Contacting us
Write to us at the address above or call us on:
Tel   0800 375 2121
Fax   0800 375 2222

Call charges for account 001752

Call charges up to 9 June 1999	4.02
Sub total for VAT	4.02
VAT total at 17.5%	0.70
Total value of this bill	£4.72

Account statement

Outstanding balance	1.81
This month's charges	4.72
Amount due	£6.53

Please note any payments made or taken in the previous 14 days may not show on this statement.

£ Estimated savings against BT standard rate

Savings on call charges this month   £1.71
Your account information

Further savings on mobile calls from DBA

As a valued customer you are benefiting from some of the lowest call charges available.

	DBA W/E	DBA Economy	DBA Standard
Cellnet	1.40	13.44	13.86
Vodaphone	5.18	10.50	14.42
One 2 One	5.60	12.53	17.71
Orange	5.53	12.46	17.36

All prices in pence per minute, VAT inclusive

We are pleased to announce that with effect from 1 January we have introduced reductions of 5%.

These reductions apply to calls made to mobile phones connected to any of the following networks.

A bill like this is a rich source of:

- Relevant information
- Numbers used in different ways
- Tables and charts
- Checking calculations for accuracy
- Scales and proportions

Using information

The bill uses numbers in a variety of different ways – as a code, as a reference and to repeat amounts. This is a straightforward bill but you should learn how to find and interpret information and check the accuracy of calculations before paying it. You may also wish to record your results for use in another context such as a letter of complaint for inaccuracies or in your personal accounts of income and expenditure.

Please check that you can read and understand the table. Do you understand the meaning of VAT?

Practising and using your number skills

Look at the key below to see if you can read, understand and use the information to develop your number skills.

1. The bill is a source of relevant information using written and graphical material.
2. These use numbers as references. You could use them when discussing the bill with the company.
3. These use telephone and fax numbers as codes. You use them when making contact with the company.
4. This is a table which gives your monthly statement.
5. This is a table with the new scale of charges. Can you draw up a table for the existing scale of charges?
6. Look at the value of the bill and check the VAT. What do you find? Have you benefited or has DBA?
7. This gives you the amount of money that should be paid. Why is it more than the total value of the bill?
8. This shows you how much you have saved by being with DBA. What would your BT amount have been and what is your percentage saving for being with DBA? If you don't know how to work out percentages, you will need to look at page 12.

Look at the new scale of charges in point 5:

- W/E means the weekend (midnight Friday to midnight Sunday).
- Economy means every 7 pm each weekday until 8 am the following morning.
- Standard means daytime between 8 am each weekday until 7 pm that evening.

Look at the bill in point 7. Calculate, to the nearest minute, how long the user could have spoken on a weekend, a weekday evening or during the day using this new scale. Do you think this is really what happened? Is it sensible?

Personal tasks and topics

You could use this type of topic to produce different levels of numerical information:

- Look at other types of telephone bills where there is a standing charge as well as call charges. Find out how much they charge per minute and compare it with this bill. A comparison could be shown on a graph.
- Look at the table given in point 9. You could represent this information graphically by showing cost against minutes.
- Information on all your bills, e.g. electricity, gas and cable TV, could be used to work out your monthly expenditure and compare it with your monthly income. This could be used to help you record and plan your personal expenses.

Graphics in newspapers

Newspapers use tables, charts, diagrams and graphs to present different types of information. Many are used elsewhere in this chapter. Three types of graphs are shown below: a bar chart, a pie chart and a pictogram.

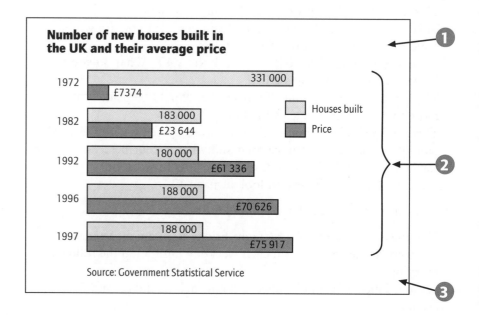

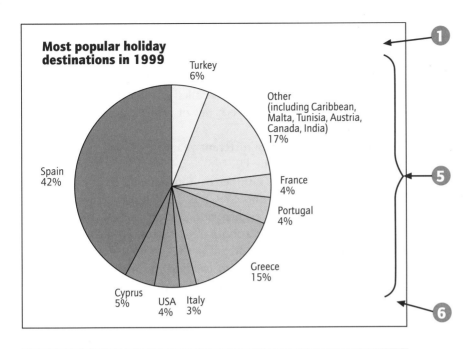

Most popular holiday destinations in 1999

- Turkey 6%
- Other (including Caribbean, Malta, Tunisia, Austria, Canada, India) 17%
- France 4%
- Portugal 4%
- Greece 15%
- Italy 3%
- USA 4%
- Cyprus 5%
- Spain 42%

The taste test: ice cream

Brand	Price	How it rates for taste
Sainsbury's soft scoop	£1.35/2 litres	
M&S soft scoop	£2.49/2 litres	
Somerfield real dairy	£1.99/1 litre	
Asda gold medal	£2.29/500 ml	
Waitrose organic	£2.69/500 ml	
Tesco very vanilla	£2.39/55 ml	

= 5 shoppers

Using information

In order that you can read and understand graphical material, use the information and the data they contain to find results and present your own findings. You need to use the correct conventions and scales.

Please check that you can read and understand the graphical material. You may need to look at page 3 to check the conventions for pictograms, bar charts and pie charts.

Practising and using your number skills

Look at the key below to see if you can read, understand and use the information to develop your number skills.

1. This type of numerical information is called graphical material
2. This is a bar chart that carries two types of information on number and amounts:
   - Numbers of houses built in different years
   - Average house prices in the UK
3. What can you say about the number of houses being built and their average price between 1972 and 1997? Work out how much money has been spent on homes for each period and set this out in a table and in a graph to enable you to compare the data. Find the mean house cost in the last 25 years and show this on your graph
4. This is a pictogram. It is arranged to provide you with data which you can compare. This one has more information than is usual as it has numerical information as well as symbols. Note the value of each chef's hat.
5. This is a pie chart that shows you how a particular activity, event or budget has been divided up. This one looks at holiday destinations for a holiday company.
6. What can you say about the most popular holiday destination? If you are told that the holiday company had 1.4 million customers, can you work out how many holidaymakers went to each destination? Present your information in a graph to compare numbers for each destination.
7. Pictograms are simple to read if you want to compare information. If you want real information you must use the key for the symbol. How many shoppers were consulted here? Why is the cost column a little confusing? Can you use the costs to present the costs for each ice-cream on the same axes for costs against litres between 0 and 5 litres? Is there any link between cost and the taste ratings?

Personal tasks and topics

This type of topic will help you develop, record and present your results and findings in a variety of different ways. When you investigate this sort of information you must always check that the graphical material uses the appropriate conventions. Newspapers do not have to follow mathematical conventions but sometimes distort presentation to emphasise a point.

Numerical information can be found relating to:

- Personal finance such as loans, pension plans or bank rates.
- General information such as the weather.
- Financial information such as share prices.
- Shopping information such as sale prices and mail order.
- Holiday information such as travel details and currency exchange rates.
- Sporting information such as results services and league tables.

Index